End
of
the
Rainbow

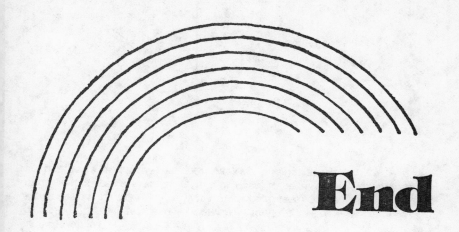

Mary Ann Crenshaw

End of the Rainbow

MACMILLAN PUBLISHING CO., INC.   *New York*

For my mother and father

Acknowledgments

How do you thank someone for saving your life? Language is far too limited, emotions far too strong. In my case, so very many people helped, in so very many ways, to make me whole again. I can only hope that this book will, if only in a very inadequate way, serve as an expression of my gratitude.

I especially want to thank Dr. LeClair Bissell for her kind encouragement and counsel during the writing of this book, and Dr. John Severinghaus for imparting to me his vast knowledge of the workings (and dangers) of prescription drugs.

I am forever indebted to Maggi, who was there and knew just what to do, and to Val and Rick, who held my hand throughout all those difficult years. And, of course, to the entire Smithers staff, who taught me more about life than I knew was there to be learned.

And then there are my friends—my incredible friends—who listened and encouraged and supported and sustained to a point far beyond ordinary friendship's limits. But, then, mine are not ordinary friends. Each of you knows what you did, each of you knows how much it mattered, and each of you knows, I hope, how very much you mean to me. Without you, I would never have made it at all.

I am so very grateful to Henry Morrison, for always being there, *especially* when I needed him. And to George Walsh, for having faith.

To all the recovered addicts who, day after day, shared with me their experiences, their strengths and their hopes, I can only offer my admiration, my gratitude, and all of my love.

I.

1.

How long had I been lying in the dark? Days? Weeks? It was dark in the room all the time, but in fleeting, conscious moments I saw, through the blinds, light and then darkness again. It meant, I guessed, another day had passed.

I lay in my bed and felt nothing. The pills saw to that. Whenever consciousness came, I shut it out quickly with another pill. I just wanted to sleep, that was all. Sleep would surely cure me.

The taste in my mouth was terrible. Sickly sweet. Bittersweet. It rose up through my nose until everything smelled of it. Why did Valium taste so bad when you took too much?

I had to remember to take the Navane. God knows, we all knew how sick I got when I didn't take the Navane on time. Eight o'clock, twelve, five. I'd have to set the alarm to make sure I woke up.

Where was Alan? Why hadn't he come to help? Or had he come yesterday? What was yesterday? I knew it was February, but what day was it?

I just needed to sleep. If only I could sleep for about twenty-four hours, I'd feel better. Surely I would.

But the damned phone kept ringing. "Did you forget our lunch date?" "I'm sick." "Again?"

God, I hated it when people sounded as if I were sick all the time. Damn them anyway. I didn't *want* to be sick in bed. I didn't want to be sick at all. And I certainly didn't want the pain.

I hurt all over, from the pit deep inside my head where my brain was supposed to be, to my throat, where a long knife had lodged, to my gut, which ached right through my ribs to my spine, to my legs, which were swept with stabbing pains.

Maybe Fiorinal would deaden the pain, and the phenobarb in it might help me sleep better, too. If I woke up, I could always take a couple of Valium. Maybe an extra phenobarb. I just had to get some sleep. If the phone would just shut up!

I hoped I would remember to take all the other stuff when I got up to take the Navane. The diuretics and the thyroid medicine for sure. I didn't have any idea what new things would go haywire inside if I forgot those.

If the pain didn't get any better, I could always take a Percodan. Or some codeine. Or both. That ought to knock the pain off its pins.

If I waited a couple of hours after the last Navane, I could take a Placidyl. That would make sure I slept at least a few hours. After all, sleep was what would make me get better.

And so days passed, but I did not get well.

I don't remember eating, though I guess I did. I don't remember seeing Alan, though he says he came.

I remember that my doctor came and went. I remember that the phone rang. I remember that the alarm rang. And I remember that I took my medicines. All of them.

And then one day, none of them helped. Not the Percodan, nor the Valium, nor the codeine, nor the chloral hydrate, nor the Placidyl, nor the Fiorinal, nor the phenobarbital. And I cried and cried until my eyes were red and swollen and I couldn't breathe. I knew I just couldn't go on anymore.

My doctor came, said we'd figure something out when I was better, and went away. Alan came and looked at me in a funny way and said he'd stay.

And that night, I looked down and saw in my hand a rainbow of pills. For the very first time, a fearful realization swept through my trembling body. I knew that in my hand I held the instrument of my very own death.

I threw the pills to the floor and sobbed into Alan's shoulder, "You have to help me. Somebody has to help me."

That was the way the nightmare ended. And that was the way the nightmare began.

2.

I am convinced of it—I was an addict in my mother's womb. Oh, not that my mother was shooting up dope, or anything like that. Far from it. My mother was a gentle, darkly beautiful Southern belle. My mother didn't know anything about addiction.

My father was a bit different. My father was the aggressive young lawyer who came out of Harvard Law School, wearing his Phi Beta Kappa key, at the ripe age of seventeen to join the family law firm. And when my father wasn't off trying cases, he was at the country club playing golf. And drinking in the cool of the dimly lit bar. As was his father. And his hard-playing bachelor brother. My father, though he didn't know it then, was learning about addiction.

I was a red-haired, green-eyed, chubby little baby who basked in the adoration of her parents and indulgent grandparents. I was, after all, the very first, very perfect child. And nobody, certainly not I, realized that somewhere deep within me, that tiny seed of addiction had already been planted. We lived in the enchanted house my father had built, at the end of a brick-covered walk, in the shadow of my grandmother Crenshaw's white-pillared home. And there I grew up in a land of zinnias and verbena, of figs and cream, of ponies and puppies, and of love.

I adored my mother and longed to look just like her, but I had my red hair and freckles while she—all raven hair and alabaster skin and soulful dark eyes—looked like a serene Madonna. My mother had inherited the dark beauty of my Irish grandmother, while I had inherited, from my Irish grandmother, something quite different, indeed.

My father, on the other hand, with his swinging gait and brisk manner, was the parent I wanted to *be* just like. I didn't know how I could accomplish that—I was, after all, a little girl—but I was determined. I knew I had inherited his looks. I did not know then that I had inherited much, much more, and would one day be just exactly like my father.

Soon my brother was born, dark-haired, and quiet, and beautiful and every bit my mother's child, while of me, everybody said, "She looks just like Jack. Acts like him, too."

In our childhood it always seemed to be summertime. But my mother cried a lot of the time, and often my father was not there. Even when he was there, he sometimes seemed not to be there. It was many years before I was to understand why.

When my childhood ended and my girlhood began, we moved into a big house all our own. It was, I thought, the most beautiful house I had ever seen. It was, we all thought, the perfect house, with its Palladian proportions, its old rose-brick walls, its white-columned portico. We were going to live happily ever after, there in our beautiful home.

But things didn't work out quite that way. For one thing, my father drank. Most of the time. And since I knew that I was the one most like my father, I felt responsible for "doing something" about that. I spent a lot of time pouring bottles of booze into the kitchen sink. I never stopped to consider that my father might punish me. I was too angry for that. Besides, I had his temper, didn't I? I knew I could fight him. I knew that I was the only one in the family who could. I knew that it was up to me to protect my mother (who cried) and my brother (who grew more and more silent). And I hated the whiskey—hated the way it smelled, hated the way it looked, hated the way it made my father look, all stupid and glassy-eyed. When he was drunk, I hated my father a lot. I knew I didn't want to be like him anymore.

The rest of my life, on the other hand, was OK. The friends I'd had since the first grade were the friends I would have all my life. In those sunlit days of our girlhood we divided our time equally between horses and boys, and we all got our share of broken hearts and did our share of heartbreaking.

There were the usual rounds of hayrides and swimming parties and proms, but never in my own crowd was there any liquor. I had tasted it once and I'd hated the taste as much as the smell. As for beer, well, I was convinced it might be OK if only I could add a little salt, but, if the truth be known, I just wasn't interested in drinking. My friends weren't either.

When I was seventeen I entered college. I took my white convertible off to the big city of Nashville, where I worked hard and played lots. The competition was fierce, and studies were what mattered most. After that came football games and fraternity dances and sorority stuff. And my Alabama home, to which I fled every two or three weekends.

At college I took my first drink—a glass of beer at the local hangout. But I still thought it needed salt, and I still didn't like it. So I just didn't drink. Neither did any of my buddies. Therefore it came as a surprise to me when, one day in a Nashville tearoom, a fortune-teller read my palm and said, "You may become an alcoholic." I laughed and said, "But I don't even drink." She replied, "That doesn't mean you won't."

By my senior year a lot had changed—my feelings about myself, about where I was going, about what I wanted to do with my life. The truth was, I didn't *know* what I wanted from life. I'd even taken a year off from school to try to work it out. That was when I became involved in a love affair that ended tragically with the boy's death in a plane crash. I saw it happen. The rest of that year was spent not so much in working out my life as in trying to work my way out of the deep, all-encompassing grief that followed. That required time and a certain amount of sedation. I finally climbed back into life's stream in Cuba, where, at the University of Havana, I made a leisurely study of Spanish and, in the *boîtes,* a study of Cuban nightlife. I learned to drink a little rum and Coke, but mostly I got high on the dancing. Only once did I get high on the rum, and I was terrified I'd pass out and be disgraced. Some strong coffee and a nap took care of that, and no one was ever the wiser.

But one hot Havana night I awoke with a start to see a huge furry tarantula scurry across my bed. I bounded from the bed, pulling the sheets and the mattress onto the floor in a heap, but there was no tarantula anywhere, not even a dead one. When I told my classmates the next day, they all laughed and said, "That old devil rum!"

And so, by my senior year in college, I was drinking rum and Coke on Saturday-night dates and at proms, but I never drank much, and I never, never got drunk.

After graduation, I "came out." I was dead set against "such childish nonsense," but my grandmother was determined to make me a proper Southern belle, so I collected lots of beautiful clothes and prepared to enjoy myself to the limit.

The social scene began with the debutante ball and lasted all autumn through gala rounds of football games, masked balls, luncheons, teas, and receptions. We danced nearly every night of the week until early morning and, in order to keep up the pace, we drank bourbon and branch water and got happily high. At least I did. I also suffered terrible hangovers, which I was convinced were due to the bourbon. Bourbon just did bad things to me, I reasoned, and I vowed thereafter to stick to rum. I never really got drunk though, because I was sure I would throw up if I did. I really drank just about like all of my friends, except for one thing—I could drink my friends under the table. Often I had to drive my dates home and they generally seemed grumpy when it happened (they were Southern gentlemen, after all) but they continued to take me out anyway. They had to. I was one of the season's debs. And I continued to drink more than they could. Even my mother said, "When you start to drink, there's no stopping you." There wasn't.

When the year was over, it was time, once again, to take stock of my life. All my friends were getting married, having met their white knights at one masked ball or another. But I hadn't found mine yet. In fact, I wasn't even looking for him. Marriage was just not part of my plan. A career, success, glamor, excitement—those were what I wanted now, what I saw as my destiny. And so, deaf to the pleas of my grandmother, who saw me as a future president of the Junior League ("It would please your father"), I packed my debut duds and left the South. I was going to conquer New York.

3.

And, in a manner of speaking, I did conquer the big city. With the combined luck of the Irish and my Aries birth sign, I landed a low-paying job in the merchandising department of *Vogue*. With an indulgent father offering financial support (to allay his alcoholic guilt, I believed), I would just be able to make it on my very tiny salary.

I found the perfect apartment, to boot—a little jewel box of a studio on a tree-lined street in the East Sixties, where the sunlight streamed in all day long and the leaves outside my window made it very privately mine. I didn't care that it was a fourth-floor walk-up. That would be good for my shape. I didn't care that it was only twelve by twelve. That was all I needed. It was minuscule, but it was mine. My father agreed to pay the $135-a-month rent. (My take-home pay just wouldn't do it.) I hoped he knew that one day, when I was more established in my chosen profession, I would pay it all back. At least as much as I could.

And so I became a New Yorker. Bona fide New York career woman, that was me. My friends back home wrote how envious they were, how exciting it all seemed. And I agreed with them. I certainly didn't envy them their lives of husbands and babies and dull, routine jobs.

I devoured New York—the theater, the parties, the restaurants, the openings, the fashion-magazine clothes (which, luckily, I could now get wholesale)—and I felt completely at home.

Settling down to the routine of my new city, I acquired all the accoutrements thereof—a dry cleaner, a butcher, a grocer who would deliver to a fourth-floor walk-up, and a family doctor.

My mother was responsible for the medical man. She believed that nobody was safe without a reliable family doctor, preferably one who made house calls. On one of her visits to check out my well-being, she called a few well-placed old school chums and came up with a doctor for me. "I just won't feel safe," she told me, "until I know you have a doctor. We never know, after all."

The doctor my mother's school friend had recommended was perfect: young, intelligent, with impeccable credentials. Most important, I liked him. I could talk to him. And yes, he did make house calls. Not that I planned on needing any.

I acquired a lot of wonderful new friends and I felt quite secure, quite settled, ever so much the young New Yorker.

And all of my friends were fun. Not one was married, not one was having babies, not one had a dull, routine job. In fact, we were all pretty much in the same lifeboat, working our ways up the old ladder of success and enjoying our climb.

Since we all liked to do the same things, we hung out together most of the time. On Saturday nights the gang came to my place, which one of my talented friends had changed from orange-crate chaotic to soft-lights-and-palm-trees romantic. (It looked, I thought, pretty darned chic for a little walk-up studio.) We relaxed from our week's labors with a few drinks, good music, and some energetic (albeit necessarily constricted) dancing. We had fun—good, clean fun—and not one of us ever conked out on booze. It simply wasn't our style. And besides, nobody ever really drank that much.

One Saturday night, however, a really strange thing happened. We'd run through our supply of Scotch, so one of the men dashed out to the liquor store for an extra pint of J & B. (Now, the fact that we needed only a pint of Scotch should give you an idea of how much we were drinking. Not much.) After the party ended, when I trudged off to the kitchen to tidy up, I discovered there on the kitchen counter a strange-looking bottle with a purple orchid on the label. It read "Margarita

Scotch." "Ye gods!" I said out loud. "No wonder I feel so drunk. We've been drinking rotgut Scotch."

But the next morning, when I stumbled, bleary-eyed and very hung-over, into the kitchen for my morning coffee, there on the counter, plain as day, was the J & B. I was shocked. Where was the "Margarita" stuff with the purple orchid? And then I realized—it simply wasn't. It was the tarantula story all over again. Another hallucination.

I was scared. Did it mean I was an alcoholic? Was I having DTs?

My doctor said, "You're probably highly allergic to alcohol. Some people are." What my doctor didn't say was that people highly allergic to alcohol are otherwise known as alcoholics.

Life went partying on. I discovered the joys of wine with meals and began sampling different wines with dinner every night. It made my beginner's cooking seem infinitely more palatable. I simply adored wine.

My job was more glamorous to the outside world than it was to me. To me it meant lots of hard work and long hours. But Friday was payday, so Friday was the day when we could count on a leisurely, luxury lunch. And so Friday was the day we drank. The guys from the art department always joined us, and we lunched from noon till three o'clock. By then I had come to love sweet mixed drinks—whiskey sours, Bacardi cocktails, daiquiris—and I drank them like lemonade. People said, "My God, you inhaled that drink!" I thought that was terribly amusing. I didn't know then that gulping drinks is a sign of alcoholism. I just knew that I wanted it right then, and then I wanted a second right away. We were all very high by Friday afternoon, and my co-workers scolded me as a bad influence. Especially when our drinks cost more than our lunch.

My drinking remained very much the same for the next few years. From time to time I grew fat (meaning ten pounds overweight) and went on a diet and gave up booze. I had never heard of a way to drink and grow thin, and I was obsessed by fat, remembering those chubby childhood days when people would say, "Isn't she cute! So plump." ("Pleasingly plump" always translated to "pretty ugly" in my head.)

But I never missed drinking at all. I was too busy watching with delight as the pounds disappeared, and I almost always felt so much better that I wondered why I ever drank. But when I got back to my ideal weight and could go back to normal eating and drinking, I always did. Drink again.

A lot had happened back in Alabama. My mother and father had at last separated. I say "at last" because they hadn't been happy for a very long time. Nobody, after all, could live with alcoholism. My father, of course, couldn't see that he was doing anything wrong. On the contrary, he always told us it was what *we* were doing wrong that drove him to drink.

I had taken myself out of that unhappy situation by leaving Alabama, but the guilt was always with me. Had I left my mother to drown in all the booze that must be backing up in the kitchen sink?

My mother had finally gotten angry. When my father threatened, for the zillionth time, to leave, she said she thought that would be a fine idea. She never let him come back home, except to collect his things.

For every depressing event in life, however, there seems to be an "up." My brother had married, and now his wife had presented him with a beautiful baby boy. My brother dubbed me "Auntie Mame." I was bursting with pride, and determined to live up to my new name. Auntie Mame indeed! "Very appropriate," my friends told me.

My life continued on its happy Manhattan merry-go-round, and soon I reached out and caught the brass ring. I fell in love.

Paolo was dashing, debonair, and drunk. He was drunk when I met him and drunk for most of our time together. But, curiously, when Paolo drank, I didn't. After all, one of us had to get both of us home in one piece, and I seemed to be the one elected.

Whenever we went out together he drank; I pleaded, cajoled, threatened, and argued, all to no avail. And when Paolo drank, he grew dark and moody and frightening.

But I loved him just the same. He was beautiful—mysterious, brooding, Latin—very different from the boys back home. He looked just like some movie star, I thought, though I couldn't decide whether it was James Mason or Gregory Peck.

I adored the fact that we communicated in his Pidgin English and my Pidgin Portuguese and (mostly) in the language of love.

Paolo and I went everywhere, did everything together, and everybody said what a handsome couple we were—Paolo with his intense, dark, good looks and me with my red hair and madcap ways. And we truly loved each other.

But a little squirrel of doubt was gnawing away at my innards. Something, somehow, seemed to be missing. And I still wasn't quite sure about the "rest of my life." Did I know absolutely that I didn't want a husband and a baby and a rose-covered cottage in the country? Could I say honestly that, with my new job and my new apartment and all my new friends and my new love, I was completely happy? That seed of satisfaction I had planted didn't seem to be growing, and I didn't know why. I decided I needed to know that truth about myself. What I needed was insight. What I needed was a shrink.

My doctor searched for me, but it wasn't easy to come up with a shrink who could see me in the evenings. And my doctor, naturally, wanted to be absolutely sure of finding a first-rate man. After all, it was my mind, and my sanity, that was at stake. He wanted to be positive.

After a month or so, my doctor said he'd finally found the man, that he was sure we'd hit it off. And we did. From the moment I met my shrink I felt safe. He was a big, woolly bear, all tweed suit and smoking pipe and squishy leather chair. I could tell he was going to help me feel better, even though I didn't know what was wrong.

Twice a week, from that day on, I spilled out my heart and my life and my love to my shrink and I relaxed a little in the knowledge that eventually I would emerge a totally happy person. Though it was going to take time.

Needless to say, my salary wasn't going to pay for a bona fide New York shrink, but my father was willing to contribute. He felt, I was sure, more than a little guilty for my being a bit confused. It hadn't been easy, after all, living with an alcoholic.

When the sixties began, a lot had changed in my life. I moved to a larger, more luxurious apartment (more in keeping with my fashion-mag image, I reasoned), and I was thinking about leaving my job. It didn't seem to be taking me where I wanted to go, although I still wasn't sure exactly where that was. And even though Paolo and I were still together, I knew I didn't want to get married. Not yet.

So we learned to twist and practiced the samba, and stood in lines to see Kennedy and Khrushchev and Castro when they visited New York. We watched as Yuri Gagarin blazed around the earth in the dark sky. And I got drunk—falling-down, throwing-up, passing-out drunk—for the very first time in my life.

I had been invited to celebrate Russian Easter with friends in the country. "We have someone we want you to meet," my host told me, so I went without Paolo, thankful that for once I wouldn't have to worry about his drinking.

The buffet was lavish. So was the bar. The Russians were all drinking vodka, of course. Straight. "Here's how you have to do it," they told me when they spied me sipping my drink warily. "Like this." They filled my glass to the top and watched as I tossed it down my throat. Then they brought me a larger glass and watched, smiling, as I did it again. And watched, still smiling (I imagine), as I was carried to somebody's car. I threw up out of the window through miles of traffic; I threw up when we reached my door; I threw up as my doorman helped me to bed.

I was humiliated. I wept on the doorman's shoulder, swearing I'd never been so drunk before (I hadn't) and that he'd certainly never seen me drunk before (he hadn't) and that I didn't know what to do (I didn't). And then I passed out. I had never done that before, either.

When I woke the next morning, still in my party clothes, I was terribly ashamed. I couldn't look the doorman in the eye. I didn't want to see my host again, and I certainly couldn't face my friends.

Alcohol had for the first time really interfered with my life. Alcohol had finally interfered with my brain and made me unconscious. Alcohol had finally become a problem.

But such problems have a way of fading with time, and, although it was many months before I could face any of the other party guests, I eventually forgot about the incident, dismissing it as a one-time thing that would never happen again.

My career got better. I had left my now-boring magazine job, feeling that surely better things awaited me in the world of fashion. And they did. For the next few years I went from glamor job to more glamorous job in chic boutiques and famous ateliers. My salaries got larger, and so did my apartments.

I lived in the East Seventies now, in a brand-new luxury apartment that looked just the way I wanted my permanent pad to look. There were velvet couches and needlepoint rugs, tall palm trees and glittering mirrors, and the walls were covered from ceiling to floor with paintings and drawings and bits of memorabilia. It seemed terribly homey to me, terribly glamorous to my friends. Most important of all, I always felt happy there.

I *was* happy, in fact, and at last I seemed to be satisfied with my life. I decided my therapy must have worked and I could dispense with it, especially now that I was paying the bills myself.

Paolo and I had drifted from love affair into friendship, but that was OK with me. I had plenty of men friends to take me out, and plenty of women friends to discuss the men with, and plenty of parties and plenty of fun. I was, I thought, the very picture of the successful and fashionable young New Yorker. Soon I would be the very picture of the successful and fashionable young executive.

I became the fashion coordinator for Ohrbach's, at a time when the store, with its copies of Paris couture, was a playground for the stylishly rich. I had a suite of offices on the executive floor, a staff of assistants, and, best of all, an expense account for entertaining. Taking fashion editors to super-posh restaurants was one of the pleasures of my job. The editors almost always ordered drinks before lunch. So did I.

But while my job was glamorous, it was also tremendously hard work and downright nerve-racking. There were photography sessions to supervise and press releases to write and always deadlines to meet. And then there were the fashion shows. I detested the fashion shows, at which I had to stand up before a crowd of Beautiful People and speak. My carefully nurtured cool always left me then, and I had paralyzing stage fright. Finally, a friend came up with a terrific little present that saved the day—a flask. Red leather, tiny, and terribly ladylike, it went everywhere in my handbag and all my cohorts knew that, whenever a fashion show was ready to run, I ducked backstage and took a big swig of Scotch. I was immediately calm, collected, and professional once more. It was our office joke. So what if occasionally I took one swig too many? I could always chase it with coffee to get back to that completely in-control state required to do the job to perfection.

But my drinking still seemed perfectly normal to me, even though I had begun to look forward to my lunchtime Bloody Marys. Begun to rely on them, in fact, even when I wasn't entertaining an editor. Even when I was lunching alone. I swore I wrote better with a drink under my belt. Perhaps I did.

My father, quite suddenly, gave up drinking. We were all enormously relieved.

My mother came to visit and was appalled to see me order a drink for lunch. I felt extremely annoyed.

4.

As the Swinging Sixties progressed, my life grew even more gala. I flew off to London to have my hair cut by Vidal Sassoon, and flew home with suitcases full of brand-new miniskirts. I danced until dawn in clubs like Arthur, where my crowd was the "in" crowd. The *Women's Wear Daily* photographer snapped me at Côte Basque and Caravelle. (I wasn't a Beautiful Person yet, but I *was* fellow press.) Pablo of Elizabeth Arden designed special makeups for my special occasions. My own parties grew larger and more glamorous: at one particularly memorable one the guest list included a bona fide Italian prince, one-third of a famed folk-singing trio, a French fashion designer, two top fashion photographers, a film producer, an English singing star, the star of a Broadway play, and a newly acclaimed novelist. My doormen routinely directed all Edwardian-looking long-haired young men to my door, and occasionally someone appeared whom I'd never seen before. The doormen thought all parties were *my* parties.

We were all having loads of fun, and my drinking never seemed any different from anybody else's. New Yorkers, I believed, led sophisticated lives and always drank at parties. Why on earth not? But in my crowd, at least, nobody ever caused a scene.

My friends at work, in fact, drank far more than I did, and I often thought that some of them were in for big trouble. After all my childhood experiences, I could recognize alcoholism when I saw it.

We always had champagne at photographic sessions, which made my store the favorite assignment for photographers and models, and we always had Bloody Marys for lunch. When the store threw a birthday bash, I got beautifully high on the punch and tried out all the newest dances. The next day, one of the stockboys passed me in the hallway and chuckled under his breath, "Go, Miss Crenshaw, go!" I wondered whether perhaps I ought to be more dignified.

But, for the most part, my superiors were indulgent. As long as I was seen in the right places, with the right people, and as long as my name and the store's made the gossip columns, I could take my always fierce hangovers to bed in the store's infirmary. I continued to work twelve hours a day, six days a week, while I danced every other night until dawn.

One day I looked in the mirror and saw myself chubby again. Oh, woe! It seemed that was going to be the pattern of my life—a few years of fun before the pounds crept back on. And overweight would never do. It just didn't go with the fashionable image. And so once more I gave up booze, even the Scotch in my little red flask. For the next six months I munched cottage cheese and drank soda water and continued to dance. I even vowed that, since my balance (and thus my dancing) was so much better, I would simply never drink again. The same thing, of course, that I always said.

In the mid-sixties, I took a giant step into my future when one of my dreams dropped into my life like a ripe apple.

I had a call one day from the fashion editor of the biggest, most beautiful, most important newspaper in New York—in the world, in fact: the *New York Times*. The venerable, good, gray *New York Times*.

Would I care to take my talents there? Well, I wouldn't really. I was having so much fun where I was that I didn't want to leave my secure little nest. But they would double my salary and that was a carrot-on-a-stick I couldn't turn down. Yes. I'd go. I'd love to.

With the new position came new prestige. The very name of the newspaper opened all doors, and where I had partied on my own name before, now I did the town from the vantage point of a reporter. My paper wanted my swinging point of view. They got it.

I was invited everywhere, to every fashion show, every luncheon, every charity ball, and every brand-new discothèque. My miniskirts grew micro, my dancing partners grew younger, my workdays grew shorter, and my parties grew bigger. Debonair, drunken Paolo disappeared into marriage. I had no time to think of such things. I just had time to have fun.

At the newspaper, everybody drank. And so did I. For I was thin by then, and my drink-free diet was over. I could booze with the best of them. And reporters can booze a lot.

It was a time of anti-war demonstrations and radical chic. I worked my tail off at the paper while I danced nonstop at clubs like Arthur and Ondine. For my favorite dancing partner had said, "Mary Ann, if we ever stop dancing, it's all over." And I believed him.

As the music world eased us into the drug culture with songs like "Paint It Black" and "Yellow Submarine," we were all wearing fake tattoos and headbands or fringes and feathers (Indians were a "cause" that year). I cut off my hair, and some said I looked just like Twiggy, while others said I looked just like a boy.

When hippies became a reportable item, I went to love-ins and be-ins and hung out with a flower child. Psychedelia was the passport to happiness, he said, but I was afraid to try mind-altering drugs. While friends flew on LSD and hashish, I kept my drugs to a trial puff of pot. I still preferred booze. But I was not a drunk. We all had wine with lunch—lots of wine. We stopped off for a drink before going home. We drank lots at lots of parties. We got high and happy. But none of us were drunks. Not yet. We were just having a high old time.

Booze, on the other hand, never seemed to interfere with anybody's work output, though I was constantly amazed by the bosses' tolerance of afternoon martini breath. In any case, everybody worked, and everybody worked hard, no matter what it was they had for lunch.

For me, work was fun. I loved the glamor of the Seventh Avenue fashion shows, where I was seated in the front row in homage to the paper's rank. I was thrilled by the sessions with the most famous photographers, the most beautiful models, the most notable celebrities. I even loved writing to newspaper deadlines. And I knew, at last, that this was what I wanted to do with my life.

The newspaper was completely different from the store, though. For one thing, it wasn't friendly. No place that huge ever is. I discovered rivalries and jealousies and tensions and bitchiness and all the things inherent in big corporate life. But I chose to stay out of things that didn't concern me, and made it a point, as I told everyone, to sit with my back to the wall at all times. To keep the daggers out.

"I Want To Hold Your Hand" gave way to "Lucy in the Sky with Diamonds." Acid rock was *the* music, and Jimi Hendrix and Janis Joplin were our kind of musicians. The glittering discos were out; the seamy upstairs club room at Max's Kansas City was the in spot in New York. My crowd was also the Warhol crowd. And if my date wanted to go home at 3:00 A.M., I kissed him good night and stayed on until 5:00. I often threw up out of the window of the taxi taking me home. I always attributed it to Max's cheap wine.

And then, one hot August night, my destiny looked me straight in the eye. And laughed.

I whirled out of a restaurant and into a collision with one of my friends, on the arm of the most beautiful man I had ever seen; I looked past a pair of yellow-tinted glasses into the bluest eyes that had ever looked into mine, and I fell in love with Alan. Who also fell in love with me.

There was, however, one large and knotty problem. Alan was married. And my friend told me he wasn't ready to break up his marriage. Not yet.

I didn't care. Marriage still wasn't part of my plan. But Alan was. And so, with my eyes open (very wide), I entered into an affair with a married man. That in itself wasn't new. Married men in New York are far more available than single ones, and I'd had my summertime flirtations. But this was different. This time I was in love. This time it would last far past summer. And hurt a lot.

I announced to everyone at work that I was now, at last, truly in love. Some were astonished. Some said they'd wait and see. Some sat back skeptically to watch. All saw me set my life on a totally different course. An uncharted course, at that.

5.

Alan was completely different from any man I'd ever known. Where my other friends were madcap and maniacal, Alan was moody and serious. Where I was talkative and extroverted, Alan was silent and introspective. We were always at opposite ends of a mood swing. But we were wildly in love.

I loved everything about Alan. His craggy good looks. The tilt of his leonine head with its thick, sand-colored hair. The steady blue-green eyes. The strong, broad shoulders. The sensitive, beautiful hands. There was a curl to Alan's mouth that I loved, too, mostly because it made him look just a little mean-and-evil. In fact, with his pugilist's nose and his yellow-tinted shades, I thought he looked just like some Mafia don. And I loved that—the fact that Alan looked a little bit wicked.

But Alan was solid. He wasn't anything at all like my slender-hipped dancing partners. In fact, Alan didn't dance at all. And he certainly wasn't anything like the shoulder-bag-swinging homosexual designers who courted the *New York Times* through me. Alan's sexuality was never in question.

And Alan wasn't a reporter, and he wasn't a photographer, and he wasn't young, and he wasn't foreign. Alan was Mr. Businessman, pin-striped suits, and all. Mr. Successful Businessman, big bank account and all. And Alan's business was enmeshed enough with my own (he'd been a journalist before he became a stockbroker) that we could talk shop. When we weren't making love.

I was impressed with Alan's worldliness and extraordinary intelligence. When Alan said to me one day, "I'm smarter than you are," I was absolutely furious, but I knew it was true. Alan had me licked on every single score.

Alan drank. He was the first three-martinis-for-lunch man I'd ever known. And we met for lunch every day. There were always martinis for him and margaritas for me, and we searched out the restaurants that served the biggest and strongest drinks. I needed something strong, to keep my feelings under control—at least through lunch. Sometimes our lunches went on all afternoon, and many times I called the office with invented appointments and said I'd be in the next day. So that Alan and I could make love and drink for the length of the afternoon.

But at night, Alan always went home to his wife while I went home alone. And, after a while, I remained at home alone, for the invitations were less frequent now that my former escorts found I no longer had eyes for them. Whenever I did go out, I drank a lot to drown my need for absent Alan, and my hangovers were always bad.

At the *Times,* things were tense. The fashion department scurried about producing more and more pictures for bigger and better fashion specials and, for the first time I could remember, we did our stories over —and over and over. The bosses seemed never to be pleased. My boss was trying to please her boss, who was trying to please the publisher, who was trying to please the public. There was an undercurrent of nervousness all around the paper. I tried to stick to my job and keep out of the dirty business of office politics.

Our deadlines were tight, the work was tough and physically wearing, and the strain on my nerves was beginning to show. I got terrible pains in my stomach, with no warning at all. They weren't new pains. I'd had them before over the years, and my doctor had done test after test after test with never any solution. Sometimes he thought it was nerves (which always annoyed me—I didn't see how such intense pain could be nerves, and I resented the implication it might be "all in my head"), and sometimes he believed it was an allergy. I tried everything from giving up eggs to doing breathing exercises, but the pains always returned with a vengeance. They seemed to come in episodes, though, and I hadn't had them for years. Now they were back to complicate my life. The one thing that seemed to soothe my tummy and make the pain easier was ice cream, so I sat at my desk and sucked on pistachio and coffee and other exotic flavors until the swelling in my belly disappeared at last. I mentioned them to my doctor, but I didn't feel like going through any more tests. Not if they weren't going to tell me anything conclusive.

My migraines (a legacy from my mother) were bothering me, too, and my doctor prescribed Cafergot, but it made me feel so bad that I finally gave it up and resorted to a long sleep in a darkened room. Fortunately, the *Times* had such a room in their infirmary.

So I ground out my stories and I met Alan every day for lunch, every evening for drinks. My heart always stopped when I caught sight of him, leaning against the doorway, waiting for me. Outside Sardi's (where they always reserved our favorite table), the autograph hunters invariably asked Alan, "Are you somebody?" I always replied, "He is."

My co-workers at the paper found it a little difficult to accept the new me. They had never seen me so euphoric, had never seen me so wrapped up in any man, had never seen me working so hard to please a man. They wondered (aloud) just where this romance was going. And I hated it (and them) when they asked me whether he had yet left his wife.

And then one day Alan tilted his head, looked at me steadily, and said, "You want someone to take care of you, don't you?" My heart stopped. No man had ever seen that before. "I want to do just that." My heart pounded. No man had ever said that before. When he said, "If I were free, would you marry me?" a heavy stone sat on my chest and didn't let me breathe, but I heard myself say calmly, "But you're not." A drum inside my brain was beating, "This is it, this is it, this is it!" as I saw myself being carried away on a white horse by a knight in yellow-tinted glasses. From that day on, my heart and my mind, my soul and my body belonged completely to Alan, to do with as he would. Because now I knew what I wanted to do with my life. I wanted to marry Alan.

6.

By late autumn something significant had happened, something that would change my life completely, though I couldn't know that then. I had embarked on another diet. But this diet was going to be very, very different.

I'd watched myself growing chubby (the ice cream, perhaps?) for a couple of months, now, and I seemed powerless to stop the on-going pounds. Although Alan thought they looked good on me, I thought I looked awful, and where fat was concerned, I never listened to anybody but myself.

Still, I hated the idea of giving up those wonderful drinks-and-wine lunches with Alan in favor of a solitary container of cottage cheese.

I was pondering the problem when a friend told me about a new doctor—a diet doctor.

I had never had any faith in "fat doctors." I thought they were quacks who shot their patients full of amphetamines while keeping them on starvation rations. I'd tried amphetamines just once, when my own doctor insisted on giving me a diet pill, and I'd had trembling and sweats for a whole week. I'd told my doctor I'd never try *that* again. I sure didn't need "speed." I was running in high gear already.

But this doctor, my friend said, was different. This doctor didn't give any kind of medicine. It was his diet that was unique. It let you eat all you wanted of the foods he approved, and you lost not only pounds but inches. Best of all, you didn't have to give up booze. All you had to give up was carbohydrates. It was the diet I had been searching for, all those cottage-cheese years.

My appointment was for the Monday after Thanksgiving. On Thanksgiving Day I ate like the proverbial condemned man, right down to the candied yams and pumpkin pie. After all, it might be my last good meal on earth.

The diet doctor did tests—lots of them—and his nurses ran in and out every few minutes for six hours, taking blood samples and urine samples and blood pressure. I was pronounced seriously hypoglycemic (meaning my blood sugar was far too low) but ready to begin my diet, which the doctor assured me was the only thing that could control hypoglycemia anyway. No more sugar for me. Ever!

When I wobbled out of the diet doctor's office, Alan was waiting with a strong arm and an offer of a steak dinner.

For the first week on my new low-carbohydrate diet, I would have to forgo alcohol completely. And, for the first time, that seemed like an impossible order. I really didn't know how I was going to get along without my drink. What I didn't know at all, of course, was that I was exhibiting one of the first serious signs of alcoholism. Dependence on a daily drink.

For that first week, I painfully gave up booze and, by the second week, I was allowed three glasses of wine a week. I spent an inordinate amount of time deciding when to drink them so as to enjoy them most. I was, by now (though I still couldn't see it) preoccupied with alcohol. And preoccupation with alcohol is one more sure sign of alcoholism.

Then the two-week trial run was over and I was (oh, joy!) free to enjoy all the hard liquor I wanted. Hard liquor, the diet doctor told me, contained no carbohydrates at all, thus was the best kind of booze. I simply couldn't believe my luck. This was the very first time in my fat-fighting life that I had been given license to drink—to drink the way I really wanted to. I did not realize that the controls that had kept my drinking somewhat in line had now been completely removed. I did not realize, then, just what an effect that would have on my life. And my future.

There was a difference in my drinking that even I could see, though. A body without carbohydrates gets drunk a lot faster than a body filled up with bread and potatoes. With nothing to soak up the booze, I was getting bombed on two drinks. That was OK, though, because by then I enjoyed getting drunk.

The days went hurtling on toward the last new year of the sixties. I threw a New Year's Eve party. All of my good friends—with the exception of Alan, of course—were there, and we drank cases of champagne and danced under a shower of confetti and streamers that came down like a magical snowfall in my cozy, cluttered apartment. We were uproariously high and ecstatically happy (though I longed to be with Alan).

The next morning my hangover and I faced an apartment ankle-deep in debris. Someone had broken an egg on the kitchen floor, and its congealed eye stared at me through dirt from an overturned plant, confetti, and cigarette ashes. I covered the mess with a newspaper until my nausea subsided, late in the afternoon.

And so the new year began like any other. Though it was to be very different indeed.

My work was grueling. The reporters cranked out stories as usual, grumbling to each other as we wrote.

Lunches with Alan were lovely, but life without Alan was not, and I grew resentful of the wife that had the man I wanted. And I grew angry with Alan for having a wife at all. But Alan said that he just couldn't leave his wife. Not yet. He was involved in a delicate business negotiation and couldn't afford the scandal of a divorce. Not now. "The timing's wrong," Alan told me. "Please be patient. Try to understand."

All I could understand was that, without Alan, I was hideously unhappy.

I decided to go back to my shrink. Although I'd gotten along without him for five years, now my life seemed out of control.

As I reeled off the things that had happened to me those last five years—the triumphs, the disappointments, the affair with Alan—my shrink puffed on his pipe, smiled his Papa Bear smile, and said, "You know, I've really missed you, Mary Ann."

And so my sessions began all over again at the beginning. Twice a week.

The shrink tried to make me be realistic about my future with Alan.

"Ninety percent of these men stay married to their wives, you know. I don't think there's really a chance in hell that he will ever leave his wife. I think you're going to have to face that." But I continued to explain to him that this was different, that Alan really loved me, not his wife, that he was just trying not to hurt her. When he could, I insisted, he would divorce her and we would live happily ever after. My shrink looked troubled and said nothing.

The *Times* gave me a special fashion section to produce on my own. Now it was up to me to show them what I could do. They emphasized that there was a lot of money riding on the project, and it had to please a lot of people—right on up to the publisher. I would have one person to help me. The deadline was a month away.

When I got home that night I poured myself a very stiff vodka and tonic. No-Cal, of course.

Alan didn't seem to be making any moves at all toward leaving his wife. I was beginning to wonder whether he ever would. At our lunches there were now often bitter arguments that never really were resolved— the same way that Alan's "delicate business deal" never seemed to be resolved. I often came back to the office with tears in my eyes. Even an after-lunch brandy couldn't stop my hands from trembling.

My shrink felt that perhaps I needed a tranquilizer. Occasionally in the past I'd tried Miltown and Librium, but I'd had adverse reactions to both of them—they made me more jittery, not less—so I'd pretty much given up on tranquilizers. But my shrink said Valium was different; Valium simply made you feel calm. I was to take one when I felt overwhelmingly nervous, and I could take it three times a day, if need be. Five milligrams, three times per day as necessary. I went to Tiffany's and bought a chic little silver pillbox for the little yellow tablets, though I hoped I wouldn't need them.

The fashion special was in full swing, and I was covering the children's market to the beat of one house every half hour. My assistant and I had to round up child models who were not only appealing and wholesome-looking but also fit into the clothes, which were not standard sizes. It all seemed one enormous complicated jigsaw puzzle that I wasn't sure I could fit together. But I knew that my job was at stake and that I'd damned well better. My stomach churned and my hands trembled most of the time. At lunchtime I guzzled glasses of wine, even when I lunched alone. Then I'd feel tired all afternoon.

I spoke with Alan every morning and again before five in the afternoon. After five, when Alan left work, there was no way for me to get in touch with him—no matter how much I needed to hear his voice.

One particular morning, Alan was nowhere to be found. No one had heard from him, no one knew what had happened. He called me at noon. "I told her about us," he said. My hands began to shake. His wife knew about us. It had been very grim. She had become hysterical, and it had taken a great deal of physician-administered sedation to get her under control again. I heard all of this as if it were coming from a voice very far away. In my mind I could see her arms around Alan, pulling him back, away from me. I heard Alan's distraught voice saying, "I just can't do this to her. I can't destroy another person's life." I put down the phone, reached in my silver pillbox, and took out a Valium. I wondered what Alan thought about *my* life.

"The damned Valium made me drunk," I told my shrink. And it had, too. I had actually had to hold on to the walls for support, I felt so dizzy. Was this the way it was supposed to work? Perhaps it was just my own reaction to the drug, but it was scary.

My shrink instructed me to break the tablet in half next time, right along the score. A half should get the effect we wanted for me. Instant calm.

The next time I felt especially nervous, I took his advice, and halved the Valium. It worked! I felt marvelous—in control, totally and completely calm. Obviously, this was the answer to my prayers. Pretty soon I found I could take a whole Valium without feeling drunk. "You've gotten accustomed to it now," my shrink told me.

As another summer rolled around, the Beatles were singing "Hey Jude," and I told Alan they were singing a message to him: "You have found her now go and get her" (meaning me). But Alan only said, "Please be patient. I'm trying to work things out." And we sat in the bar and listened to "Hey Jude" over and over again, as sung by the Beatles and by Wilson Pickett and finally by Der Bingle himself. While Neil Armstrong stepped onto the moon and Ted Kennedy tried to explain Chappaquidick to *his* wife. But every Friday afternoon that summer, Alan left for weekends with his wife while I waited alone in my apartment for Monday, holding on to Alan's words, "Wait for me, I love you so much."

I was still on the no-carbohydrate diet (in my typical over-emphatic way I had kept the carbos to zero in hopes of quick results) and, though I was as slim as I wanted to be, I found that getting *off* a no-carbohydrate diet wasn't so easy. A couple of inadvertent slips had made me swell up with six pounds of bloat overnight. I was frightened by it, but the diet doctor assured me it was merely water retention. This was how the diet worked, and I should simply stick to his diet for the rest of my natural life. "It's your new way of life," he told me. And, he added, with my hypoglycemia, I really had no choice.

The only problem was that, from the beginning of the diet, my migraines had gotten worse. When I asked the diet doctor, he said cryptically, "They'll go away when you can have a little bread." But they didn't. They got worse.

My regular doctor prescribed Fiorinal for the excruciating migraine pain. It was a marvelous concoction of aspirin and barbiturate—the better to salve the nerves and ease the terrible tension that always worsened migraines. Every time the pain in my head began, I thanked God for the Fiorinal and wondered how I'd ever survived without it. If I took two at the very first sign of a headache I could sometimes even head it off at the pass. The Fiorinal went into my pillbox with the Valium. I had no trouble keeping them apart. Fiorinal were big and white and marked "Sandoz."

But there were other head pains that even Fiorinal didn't seem to dull. Hangover headaches. Thanks to the booze allowance of the diet and my diet-induced intolerance of alcohol, my hangovers were, by now, horrendous, and they produced crippling migraines that sometimes lasted as long as three days. Even my doctor agreed with me that no hangover should last that long. It must be something else.

He thought we ought to experiment with antihistamines, because some headaches are actually allergic reactions that mimic migraines. "Allergic?" It triggered a long-ago memory of a bottle with a purple orchid on the label. Of course! I was still allergic to alcohol. That must be it. Great! I wouldn't have to suffer through those hideous hangovers anymore. And I went off to fill another prescription.

My friends, when I told them, laughed and said, "Well, now you've got a pill for everything."

7.

Alan was going away with his wife. My mind skidded into a spin-out along the floor. "I owe it to her . . . to us all," said the voice on the phone. "I have to see whether we can make it work." I heard, from far off, a tiny wail that grew into a howl of pain, and I recognized it as my own voice. "Oh God, no, please, God, please wait! I have to see you, Alan, please! I don't want to live. . . ." But Alan said, "I have to go now, they're boarding the plane. I'll call you in two weeks." And he hung up.

The receiver fell to the floor, and I quivered convulsively as if some giant hand had me by the shoulders, shaking me until my teeth rattled. My teeth *were* chattering and my cold hands trembled as the keening noise continued. Alan couldn't have left me. He *couldn't* be gone. God, please help me. Somebody, please help me.

My shrink. He would help me.

My shrink's voice was quiet and calm as he told me to see him in the morning. "I can't wait until morning," I gasped. "I can't. I don't want to go on living. I can't take it. Please. . . ." It would be better, I sobbed, if I simply stepped out of the window. At least it would be over at last. "Listen, Mary Ann," he soothed, "you're not going to step out of any window. Listen to me." And he told me to take two Valium and call for someone to be with me. He would check with me in a little while.

But I didn't want anyone with me. I wanted to die. My breast, where my heart had once been beating, felt empty. My stomach had slid away. My arms and legs had no feeling at all. I felt dead already.

Shakily I steadied myself against the wall and groped my way into the kitchen. I swallowed the two Valium tablets, just as I'd been told. Then I poured myself a glass of vodka.

The booze felt warm and good, and suddenly I knew that my stomach was still there. My heart began to beat once more, and the sobs and the trembling all stopped. All of a sudden I felt terribly tired. I would go to bed. Maybe I could sleep. That way I wouldn't have to think. I could just sleep until it was over.

I didn't go to work for two days, pleading the flu. The truth was I felt too dreadful, looked too dreadful, to go out in public. My eyes were puffy and red from crying, my head ached incessantly, and I could not, or would not, eat. I got through the lonely, empty days by taking a Valium every four hours. Plus, of course, Fiorinal for my awful headache.

At the end of the two weeks, Alan called. The trip had been a miserable failure. The marriage was unquestionably over. He knew, now more than ever, that he loved me. "But I just can't leave the children yet," Alan said. "They're too young. I can't just ruin their lives."

When I saw Alan again, our truce was an uneasy one.

8.

It was the beginning of a new decade, and the seventies, everyone was saying, were full of promise. I wondered. Nothing was the same in my life. For one thing, I had stopped dancing.

The drug culture had claimed two of my closest friends. One, a promising young fashion designer, had swallowed a bottle of tranquilizers and then stepped off a twentieth-floor parapet to his death. The other, a talented artist, died at thirty-four—his heart turned to gelatin by a constant diet of uppers and downers. Amphetamines followed by tranquilizers.

And there were others. A photographer found dead in his studio three days after an accidental overdose of pills. A beautiful twenty-one-year-old model who, in the LSD-induced belief that she was a bird, flew out of a tree and broke her neck. And others who were only half dead. A pre-Alan escort hooked up to life-sustaining equipment, his intestines perforated by speed. And a former co-worker, now wandering the streets unseeingly, her mind turned to mud by drugs. When we passed, she did not know me. Every day there was someone else.

Alan and I had been together for two years now. Together? Well, he still lived at home with his wife, and we fought constantly. He would not leave his wife. He could not leave his children, he said. He did not love me, I said. But we couldn't stay apart for long, so the affair continued. And I was miserable. When we were together, we argued; when we were apart, I drank and, since when we were apart I was now alone, I also drank alone.

My nerves were frayed all the time, but I had the means to correct that. I had the Valium. When I swallowed it, the heart that was up in my throat went back down into my chest and I could feel relatively normal again.

Things at the office were chaotic. The paper was pleading financial difficulties, and there were cutbacks in staff all around. My own position wasn't threatened—I was union—but as others were let go my duties became heavier. There were no longer any carefree days filled with excitement and laughter and joy. They were all long and exhausting and cheerless now. Nobody seemed to be able to please the powers that were, and so we did our jobs not just once, but over and over and over until the phalanx of bosses was satisfied. By then, we usually weren't happy with what had become of our work.

Like automatons, we marched up and down Seventh Avenue, writing up fashion shows, selecting the clothes for those endless photography sessions, going on sittings, and lugging hundreds of pounds of clothes all over town. (For by then reporters were acting as messengers as well, to save the paper money.) Then we wrote and filed our stories and started all over again on the next ones. Nobody in my office smiled anymore.

I wasn't lunching with Alan every day now. We were both far too busy. I lunched most days with Erica, my friend from Book Review, who was as disgruntled with her department as I was with mine. At our local bistro the waiter brought us each a double glass of wine before he brought the glasses of water. After the first two doubles, we felt a bit better and so we dallied while we had two or three more.

When Erica couldn't join me I lunched there alone, mostly because I really needed that noontime wine. I wasn't alone, though, for the little bistro was the local pub for the paper people. And everybody drank lunch.

Afternoons at the newspaper were spent in a cloud of martini and/or Certs breath. Yet we all continued to do our jobs while the newspaper remained a model of respectability.

I felt as if the sword of Damocles dangled over my head at all times. It did, in fact. The new boss didn't like me, but she couldn't dismiss me. All she could do was make my life as miserable as possible in the hope that I would leave on my own. She partially succeeded. I was miserable, all right, and jittery—but I had the pillbox and I took pains to have it filled with Valium all the time. Sometimes I shared my wealth with my equally nervous co-workers. Then, for an hour or so, we would have a modicum of drug-induced tranquility.

9.

By the summer of 1970 everything had changed. My favorite dancing partner had gone off to live the good married life in suburbia. Paolo and his wife were back in Brazil, producing a baby a year. I hung out with a handsome, heterosexual hairdresser who served as friend, confidant, and go-between for Alan and me.

My relationship with Alan now fluctuated between wild love scenes and even wilder fights. The fighting was especially vicious when we drank, which was, by now, often. One terrible night, in the midst of a bitter argument, I struck Alan hard, full in the face. The force of the blow sent his glasses flying in an arc to the floor and, screaming like some unleashed harpy, I leaped forward and came down on them with my heel. And then I saw my dreams lying there in a pile of yellow-tinted dust. I sank to my knees and sobbed from my breaking heart as Alan closed the door behind him without another word. But the affair was not over, though I prayed for it to end. I simply could not bear much more pain. I goaded Alan, trying to make him admit that he really loved his wife after all. When he finally admitted that—and I had no doubts that one day he would—then I would be able to get on with my own life. What my own life would be, however, I did not know.

All my friends seemed uncertain about what to do with their lives. It wasn't only the newspaper crowd that was job-disgruntled. We all seemed to be searching for something that was eluding us. Something like contentment.

We were tired out with partying—it didn't seem much like fun anymore. We should, we felt, settle down a bit, lead more responsible lives, like mature, grown-up people. But first we had to decide what we wanted to do about summer. It was upon us, and we wanted to enjoy this first summer of the new decade before we settled down to whatever our lives were going to be. We began to talk tentative plans.

Alan had taken a house at the beach for his family. Well, damn it!, if Alan was going to make me into a mistress, then he ought to *keep* me like a mistress. And *this* summer, I wasn't going to weep alone in the city every weekend while he made love to his wife under a beautiful beach moon. (For this was my fantasy.) No, damn it! If his wife had a beach house, then I was going to have a beach house—and it sure as hell wasn't going to be any shack. It would be the very best the fashionable Hamptons had to offer. Alan agreed: I should get the very best.

10.

We found the perfect house. A beautiful old barn, right in the middle of a potato field, with a perfect view of the sunset. There were trees shading a clipped green lawn, flowers in tubs, and roses trailing over rail fences. The big barn doors slid open to an enchantment of white stucco walls, a free-standing fireplace, and cool slate floors. It was a dream house, and it was going to be ours.

For I had found the perfect people to share my summer. Responsible young people, just like me. Greta and Nils, a young Danish couple (he, a photographer, she, a fashion designer) and their close friend Mark, a handsome young film-maker who would be in residence with his current love. They were my kind of people, all right, and, like me, they were eager to get away from all the razzle-dazzle houseparty life of summers past. They, like me, wanted their own place in the sun. They, like me, wanted a calm and comfortable summer before settling down to the new "seventies" life-style. Whatever that was.

I volunteered to take the only single bedroom. It was my gesture of faithfulness to Alan.

For the next weeks, we all chattered excitedly to each other by phone, planning our summer strategy. And it looked good. For one thing, we were going to know a lot of people in the Hamptons that year. One of my closest friends, Sarah, and her husband had taken a large and luxurious house down the road. There was an attractive-looking man renting the house next door. Our friendly landlord and his swimming pool were two houses away, and all up and down our road there were people of waving acquaintance. We were invited to the first big socially important party of the season. We were all thrilled with the propitious beginnings of our summer. Life was beginning to look pretty good once again.

I bought myself a sports car. So what if it was a five-hundred-dollar used car? It was still a snappy-looking little green Fiat just big enough for two (well, maybe three, if the back seat passenger stayed supine). Alan grandly offered to buy my first tankful of gas—all six gallons of it—and I happily drove off into summer. It was, I was sure, going to be swell.

At the paper we were frantically busy. May was our busiest season and the month when we produced the special fashion sections for fall. Once again I had the dubious honor and hard work of editing the children's section myself.

The photographer and I spoke to each other seemingly hundreds of times a day. Somewhere we were going to have to do the actual photographs, sandwiched in between the shows, using clothes we could keep for only a couple of hours at a time. And, of course, we had to work around the children's school schedules. The deadlines were brutal, the hours were punishing, and everybody's nerves were twanging. We had no time for relaxed lunches (with or without Alan), and meeting for drinks post-work was out of the question since we never knew when we'd wrap it up. I simply pushed myself on toward exhaustion and then cabbed it home to collapse and to relax, at last, with a drink.

I had learned a neat trick. If I kept a bottle of vodka in the freezer, then it would be that perfect, icy cold necessary to make the perfect, icy martini. Trouble was, I didn't really like martinis. And besides, they were entirely too much trouble. It was far easier simply to open the freezer door and take a long swig right out of the bottle. Get right to the point, so to speak, which was instant relaxation.

Somehow, though, I never managed to relax. For one thing, the phone never stopped ringing. When it wasn't my friends calling to gossip, it was my assistant calling with yet another problem. The problems, in fact, never went away, and I took them to bed with me each and every night.

Of course, the more problems I had to solve in bed at night, the less I slept. And the more insomniac I became, the more frantic I was to find something that would help me to get the sleep I knew I so desperately needed. Required, in fact.

I soon discovered that two Valium plus a couple of swigs out of that vodka (or Scotch, or whatever was around) would temporarily dispel the problems in my head and send me to sleep as soundly as a baby. But it was getting harder to wake up in the morning, and I never felt bright-eyed and bushy-tailed, that was for sure.

I discussed the situation with my shrink, who thought he had the answer—a new kind of sleeping pill that was not a narcotic but a hypnotic. It could give me sleep and sweet dreams for about eight hours, and there would be absolutely no hangover. I was thrilled! God, was it possible I had really found a permanent solution to my sleep problems? I left his office with a prescription for Placidyl, five hundred milligrams.

It was a wicked-looking capsule, blood-red and gelatinous, but I took it with absolutely no qualms. My shrink knew all about my peculiar drug reactions and he'd said "no hangover." I crawled into bed and knew no more until my eyes flew open the next morning. Fantastic! This, then, was the answer to insomnia. To *my* insomnia, anyway. Placidyl, bless you.

Placidyl did not go into my little silver pillbox, however. I wouldn't need to take it during the day. Placidyl was put in the medicine cabinet, to be doled out, one capsule per night. Ah, precious, wonderful, sound, and restful eight-hour sleep.

11.

I couldn't wait for the beach season to begin. I knew I needed it badly. Well, I knew I needed something. My life felt so fragmented. Half of my energies were directed into my job, half of my energies were directed into my relationship with Alan and half of my energies were directed into deciding what my new and more pulled-together life would be. The trouble was, it all added up to more lives than I had to give.

I was feeling physically exhausted, and my mind was fuzzy. It was hard to come up with fashion stories week after week, and I found it hard to be enthusiastic about pinning up models' hemlines. Photographic sessions now seemed more grueling than exhilarating.

My relationship with Alan was strained and I found it difficult to know how he really felt about me. We still made love often and it was always beautiful, but then Alan always went home to his wife, and the pain returned to my heart. When the pain returned, I usually drank. I just couldn't deal with all those hurtful feelings. It had become my pattern, in fact, on the nights when I wasn't meeting Alan, to come home and settle down by the telephone with a regularly replenished drink. By the time I'd finished making my nightly check with my friends, I was feeling happily high. Sometimes I felt so good I didn't even bother to eat at all.

On nights when Alan and I fought—which was almost every time we discussed the fact that he hadn't yet left his wife—we both drank, and when we drank we fought more bitterly. When I was home alone with the anger, I got deliberately and totally drunk. Somehow I just couldn't wait to get home so that I could finally let out all the rage in private. On those nights, I locked the door and turned off the phone and reached for the vodka. I didn't care how drunk I got, I didn't care how I felt the next day, I didn't care about anything at all. In fact, nothing at all was the only thing I *did* care about. I wanted to feel nothing at all. I wanted oblivion.

But the next day, the pain was still there, coupled with a horrendous headache and hideous sick hangover. My relationship with Alan was no clearer, and I still wasn't sure where my life was supposed to be going. My shrink and I talked about it, but never seemed to reach any resolution. I hoped that summer would work out all the tension and kinks in my body *and* in my mind. Maybe after this summer we would *all* know where we were headed.

By Memorial Day weekend we were firmly ensconced in our barn and set to give our very first party. Young, chic Hamptonites, *chez nous*. We'd already made friends with loads of "summer people" in the neighborhood and, in fact, in all the chic little enclaves the length of the Montauk Highway. They had, apparently, liked our barn as much as we did, and the troops marched in and out of those big barn doors at all hours of the day (and night). The cast of characters was colorful, all right! There was a young sculptor and her California beach-boy lover who shared a "shack" on surfers' beach and came to us for their daily dose of elegant living. A thoroughly married (thirty years), thoroughly mad lawyer couple who owned a posh spread in East Hampton but found that spot too sedate for their lively ways. A beautiful on-the-prowl fashion model who'd taken the most expensive right-on-the-water house in Bridgehampton and filled it with an ever-changing cast of assorted and omnipresent house guests, many of whom she deposited with us. And, of course, our next-door neighbor, who turned out to be the most sought-after stage director in New York. They were all our kind of people and, it turned out, most of us had mutual friends in the city. We all lived the same sort of lives, freewheeling and, we believed, fun.

And so, on the holiday Saturday night, Greta, Nils, Mark, and I prepared to establish our reputation as the house with the best parties in the Hamptons. We invited everybody we knew, everybody we invited came, and everybody who came brought guests. The barn was a madhouse. There were filmmakers and film stars, rock musicians and rock groupies, beach bums, social lions, and seamy sorts. There was *everybody,* and everybody seemed to be having fun. There was every sort of booze imaginable, and the surfer brought his good, strong grass, which he graciously passed out to one and all. The music was blasting and the conversation a din.

At the height of the party mania, someone pulled me aside and said, "Mary Ann, I am so happy to see you've finally hooked up with some normal people." I couldn't stop laughing. Normal? Everyone was wild-eyed and pie-eyed. Those who weren't bombed on alcohol were zonked on something else. The air was blue with marijuana smoke. The music was at eardrum-damage decibels, and it seemed to spur people on to insane antics. A gay decorator was chasing the fashion model around the room and when she eluded him, he took up the chase behind the rock star. Greta had fallen asleep on the sofa, in what I would soon learn was her normal party stance. The lawyer couple was embroiled in a knock-down argument. Normal? I hoped not. Normality was dull. My new friends were chic, responsible young maniacs. That was why this summer was going to be so much fun. In the autumn, we would all really settle down. But to normality? Well, I wasn't sure I really wanted to go *that* far.

When the crowd thinned and finally disappeared near dawn, it was clear that we had a hit on our hands. In fact, our house was the house to hit if you wanted to have fun in the Hamptons that year. We were delighted. We were, as we'd planned, chic, responsible, and fun young hosts.

In a short time our summer-house routine was established. All four of us were determined that ours was to be a hassle-free house, with none of the infighting that often ruined shared-house summers. We were each going to know our jobs, each going to share in the costs, and each going to let the others be. We all just wanted peace and calm and joy, while we worked out our now-and-future life-styles. And the little roles we each would play were beginning to be apparent. Mark, for example, wasn't going to be around much. He'd dumped his girl friend right after Memorial Day weekend and now was on the hunt for a replacement. When he wasn't pursuing the model, he was surfing with the California beach boy. We could pretty much cross off Mark as a reliable source of anything other than charm. Greta and Nils could be relied on for solidity. ("Isn't that what marriage is all about?" I said to myself.) And as for me, I wasn't looking for anything more than a bit of rest. I was, after all, committed to Alan, and I had no plans to be unfaithful to him now. My little single bedroom was sacred territory. I was available only to add yet more stability to our household.

Every Friday night, we arrived in separate two-seaters. For me the trip was an ordeal because I had to pass the exit that Alan took to get to his marital love-nest on another part of Long Island. I always tried to look the other way to avoid seeing the sign, as if not seeing it would mean not hurting.

Generally Greta and Nils were the first to arrive, and they had a fire blazing by the time Mark and I drove in. Mark always had a different beautiful blonde with him, and it took us the better part of the evening to get acquainted with each new one. I tried to make sure I had at least a traveling companion for each different Friday night, even if it had to be just someone needing a ride. Anything to get me safely past the exit to Alan's house.

When we'd all unpacked and settled around the fire, we poured our glasses of wine and sat back to unwind from the rigors of the week. Depending on the number of people spending the weekend, our gabfest lasted anywhere from two in the morning to dawn (and, depending on the lateness of the hour, got us anywhere from relaxed to hilariously high). I always tumbled into bed exhausted, and although I'd always downed my share of wine, I never risked not getting to sleep. I took my prescribed Placidyl every night, just in case.

By 8:00 A.M. we were all up again. Greta and I did the shopping for the weekend, taking the money from the kitty for our forays into the village. Trying not to lose precious Saturday sun time, we finished the shopping quickly, then zoomed off to the liquor store to stock up on wine—gallons of it. We were all on diets, and not really intent on heavy, hard drinking. Not in the sun at the beach. But we loved our white-wine spritzers.

After a couple of vicious group hangovers, we decided that everybody's favorite Almaden Chablis was the culprit. "Loaded with chemicals," somebody said. So we opted for three gallons of Gallo and assorted other jug wines. That would be enough to last the weekend.

That was the sunniest summer in recent history. We lay on the beach all day long, sipping white-wine spritzers while we toasted our tired bodies. Let other houses bring ceremonial pitchers of Bloody Marys. *We* weren't, we vowed, that all-fired interested in booze.

12.

Weekends were a breathing space in my life. They put me in another time and another place, where I didn't have to dwell on my problems. The city was another matter. Back in the city, I was miserable. Things were just not the same with Alan.

When I asked Alan what was happening to our great love he was noncommittal, and every Friday afternoon he left to join his wife in the country. Sometimes he left even before lunch. Almost as if he couldn't wait.

I walked around with a dull pain in my heart that never went away.

Our office was in a turmoil. One of my cohorts in the fashion department had crumpled under the pressures that were beginning to affect us all and one day, after twenty years at the paper, she simply packed up her things and resigned. We were all terribly upset. She had seemed like the sanest, most dependable member of the staff. She didn't drink, she didn't dance, she didn't oversleep, she was never hung over, she was never sick, she didn't take tranquilizers, she didn't rush off for long weekends, she didn't fight with her husband, she didn't fight with us, she didn't complain. But she left, and was never seen again.

I took up the slack while my boss kept her bosses at bay. We worked under tension as well as deadlines. It was no fun at all now. In fact, it was hell.

My stomach pains were bad. When they came—and I could never tell what triggered them—there was nothing I could do but lie on my bed, trying not to move, while the tears poured down my cheeks. I had never had to endure pain so intense, so unbearable.

My doctor kept saying it had to be nerves, which seemed to me an excuse for his inability to find what was wrong with me. Anyway, I didn't see how it could be nerves. Not when the pains often awakened me in full intensity, from the middle of a Placidyl-sound sleep.

I begged my doctor to try again to find a cause.

We started all over. Gallbladder X-rays, upper GI tract X-rays, lower GI tract X-rays. Zilch. Nothing. Zero. My gut seemed to be functioning just fine. But the pains wouldn't go away. I needed something to ease the pain. What I got was Percodan.

Percodan was an extremely strong painkiller, my doctor warned me. It ought to do the trick. One every four hours until the pains subsided.

Percodan turned out to be as good as my doctor's word, and usually not only deadened the pains but put me out for a few hours so that I could sleep it off. By the time I awoke I usually felt better, but the soreness in my belly always lasted for days.

Big, yellow Percodan went into my pillbox with the Valium and the Fiorinal. I was glad the pillbox was reasonably commodious, since I wanted to have the Percodan with me all the time.

But on the off chance that my doctor had been right and that it really was my nerves that produced the awful pain, I tried to keep as calm as possible with Valium. If I felt the stomach pains starting, I always took two Valium at once, as a sort of warding-off insurance.

As the summer moved into full heat, my life seemed to move into racing gear. But I wasn't sure that it was exactly on course. For one thing, it was still so terribly fragmented.

Oh, it was great to be able to get away to the barn every weekend. It gave me a much-needed respite from all my problems. I could escape into a silly, carefree beach scene where our biggest problems were such things as which Saturday-night party to attend.

And on weekends I didn't have to worry about whether I would hear from Alan. I knew I wouldn't hear from Alan.

But, while the weekends were a life-giving breath of country air, they still splintered my life into pieces that ricocheted around like some miniature nuclear explosion. A fissioned life, that's what it was, entirely taken up with going to or coming from the country, or getting ready to do either.

I never felt particularly well any more. Something, somewhere, always seemed to hurt just a little. I tried to kill the pains with a bit of booze and/or a pill.

For the first half of the summer, we had fun in our barn. Greta and Nils had become my closest friends, both in the country and the city. I bent Greta's ear constantly about the Alan situation and dear, calm, quiet Greta always agreed with me completely: Alan was a shit. But then, most men were. She had had her share of problems with Nils, but they were over now. Men always came back to the women who really loved them. Perhaps Alan was just going through a phase. He would eventually leave his wife. If he didn't leave within a reasonable time—though we never established the limits of "reasonable"—then I should simply forget him. Put him out of my mind.

Mark had taken up residence more or less permanently with a gorgeous six-foot-tall German model. Beate saw my situation somewhat differently. "Fat City," she snarled. "Alan's in Fat City. He's got you both. Dump him!" I had to admit she had a point.

I had grown close to Frannie, the model. We spread out our towels together on her private beach and spent our sun time discussing the pros and cons of Frannie's latest conquests. And, of course, discussing the cons of my relationship with Alan. Frannie had no patience with Alan at all and thought he wasn't being fair with me. She called him "The Big Apple" and every time she heard another Alan story she'd say, "Let's put out a contract on The Big Apple." I had a feeling she could've accomplished it, too.

Her big house with its steady stream of guests helped make the weekends a continuous house party. If we got tired of our own crowd, we could always pop over to Frannie's, where there was a good supply of new faces, constant activity, and strong grass.

Every Saturday night, somebody gave a party and everybody got drunk—whopping, roaring, laughing (but never offensively) drunk. Oh, Greta would conk out on the sofa, never once seeing Nils make passes at all the girls. Mark and Beate usually retreated to the beach to do whatever it was they did. The lawyers always began with a fight and ended with cuddles and kisses. And I? Well, I always flirted outrageously with one man or another. I didn't want to think about Alan. I wanted some other man to want me. That would make me feel better. I also hoped it would make Alan feel worse. For that reason, most of my own house guests were men. Oh, occasionally one of them would end up in the single bed in the single room that was my gesture of fidelity to Alan. But nothing much ever happened there. We were always too drunk for that.

I thought, of course, that it was all wonderful, high-spirited fun. It was sort of my Zelda Fitzgerald image. *Zelda* was on the best-seller list that summer, and all of my friends remarked, "God, Mary Ann! Sounds just like you." That secretly pleased me a lot.

By midsummer, as we knew each other better, our lives had become less encumbered by social conventions. Everybody did what he damned well pleased, but there were some little tensions turning up in our compound. Greta and Nils were having terrible arguments, and from time to time there were shouts from their bedroom, then silence and then weeping and then, much later, Greta emerging looking mussed up and swollen-faced. I didn't know what was going on between them, and Greta never said.

Nils wasn't speaking to Mark because of some real or imagined barb he'd directed at Greta. And virtually nobody wanted anything to do with Mark's latest blonde, who looked more floozy than model.

I found myself uncomfortable in the role of go-between—a role I played to the hilt in order to keep some semblance of peace. After all, I had taken the house to put some peace and order into my life. I didn't want a lot of summer-house hassles to spoil that.

The lawyers were fighting like hell, and occasionally one or the other would reel in, dead drunk, to weep into our wine and tell us about their troubles. A couple who lived down the road were having such battles that on a quiet night the noise of crashing china and breaking glass could be heard all the way to our house.

The surfer felt discriminated against by Frannie, who made clear she thought him a bum, and the sculptor was talking to no one as she prepared for her one-woman show in September.

We were all tired, all getting a little bit nervous. Summer was already half over and our lives still hadn't fallen into place. And so we drank a little bit more and we smoked grass all the time. And I kept my cool the Valium way.

Back at the paper, the midsummer lull gave us some breathing space. Everybody around the office seemed intent only on getting away on time Friday afternoons to acquire a tan before summer ended. I felt more relaxed at work now than I felt at home. At home I felt terrible.

When Alan didn't call, I didn't know what to do. Should I wait around in case he did? Or should I find somebody else to hang out with? (Trouble was, all the somebody-elses I knew had already found somebody else.) Most of the time I just rushed home from work and hurried to the refrigerator. I knew I had a companion in there. My bottle of frozen vodka.

A couple of times I was unnerved by friends' remarks: "Gee, you sounded looped last night!"

"Last night? When?"

"When we talked."

"We talked?"

"Sure. Don't you remember?"

I didn't.

13.

To the outside world, I had everything under control. I had never looked better in my life. The diet had done its work—my weight was right where I wanted it, and Mark had described my shape as "dynamite." I had the first real tan of my life, and my hair had bleached out in the sun, making me look like the original golden girl. To the rest of the world, I was a golden girl in other ways as well. I had a job that was the envy of everyone in my profession. I had a beautiful apartment in town, a beautiful barn in the country, a beautiful little car, and a beautiful man. (For Alan was still very much in my life, and when we were out together we made, people told me, a beautiful couple.)

The world as viewed inside my head, however, did not seem so golden. On the contrary, I saw it as if through a kaleidoscope. Fractured, with a piece of me inside of every prismatic shard. And, as the kaleidoscope of my life turned, those pieces tilted this way and that, but they never seemed to come together to make the whole me.

I complained that I felt like a puppet on the end of a string, jerked to Alan when he wanted me, jerked away when he wanted *her*. Jerked to the country on Fridays, jerked to the city on Sunday. And I never seemed to accomplish anything in any place.

Sometimes, in fact, I even wished that summer were over. I was so very, very tired. Tired all the time, it seemed, in spite of the bottles and bottles of vitamins I dipped into every morning.

I was tired, also, of my weekend life. Tired of the parties, tired of the drinking, tired of the hangovers, tired of the early-morning phone calls from strange men whose sex lives I'd promised to straighten out at some unremembered party the night before. Tired of the mornings after such parties, when I couldn't find my car keys or my shoes. And tired of ending up in bed with men I really didn't relish. I was more than tired—I was frightened—when I awoke one morning with a perfect stranger by my side. It didn't matter that the stranger was attractive and gentle and massaged my hangover headache away. What did matter was that I didn't remember how he had got there. But then, neither did he.

I questioned my own behavior. Was I becoming amoral, after all this time? Had something happened to the small-town Southern morals I'd protected so diligently all those years? Or was I just stepping in time with the sophisticated social set I'd so easily slipped into? I just didn't know.

There was no one to point out to me, then, that the changes I saw in myself were only the moral manifestations of a terrible, crippling disease that took charge of my life, there in those months of summer. Nobody saw that at all.

14.

I had acquired a new admirer and was trying my best to convince myself that I was in love. I thought that if I could manage to fall in love with someone else—someone more suitable, preferably not married—then I would fall out of love with Alan. Just about then, Geoffrey, resplendent in tennis whites, walked across our lawn and into my life.

Geoffrey was very tall, very dark, and very intense (romantic, I thought). He was, he told me, trying to pull himself out of the depression of his recent divorce (I had a broken romance, too, I told him; we had something in common). Was it possible our lives had crossed through twin emotional crises? Could I possibly love him? Within five minutes of our introduction, Geoffrey kissed me resoundingly on the mouth, while my housemates looked on in amazement.

I was intrigued. God knows, Geoffrey's ardor was far removed from Alan's icy coldness. It was a hell of a lot more my style. I decided right then and there that Geoffrey was going to be the new man in my life. The right man for me.

Geoffrey was a writer—a novelist. But Geoffrey was different from most writers. He was rich. Very, very rich. And it wasn't the self-made money that Alan had acquired. It was old New York money, and with it came old New York social status. ("You have to remember I wasn't brought up a gentleman," Alan always said.) Geoffrey was everything my mother had taught me I deserved. My kind of man from my kind of family. I couldn't believe he was happening to me.

He was, in fact, happening to me with a swiftness that knocked me a bit off balance, but I didn't question it. Geoffrey said he was in love with me. I was determined to love Geoffrey in return.

My friend Erica, in Book Review, said, "Oh, Mary Ann, don't be ridiculous. Geoffrey's not your type." I huffily said I didn't agree.

I moved, temporarily, into Geoffrey's Greenwich Village town house. We had a lot of living to do in the three weeks before Geoffrey left for Europe. There'd be a lot of Europe this year, he told me. Research for the new book. I silently cursed the new book. We were, after all, just beginning to know each other.

We wandered the streets of the Village, ate in dark little bistros, drank bottles of champagne before we boarded our pink cloud back to Geoffrey's house, where we made love in a huge, old canopied bed. ("Oh, it's been in the house forever," said Geoffrey.)

On weekends, Geoffrey didn't come with me to the country. He went to Cape Cod to visit his two children, while I went to the beach alone and marveled that for a whole week, I hadn't thought about Alan. When the three weeks were up, Geoffrey kissed me long and hard, boarded his plane, and left. He'd be back in a month; he would write every day. And he did.

Alan wanted me to have dinner with him. I wanted him to see that it was all over between us. But when I told Alan that I was in love with Geoffrey, his expression never changed at all. And when, at my apartment, Alan wanted to make love to me, I let him.

By August I was seeing Alan once again. I really didn't know why except that I couldn't seem to shake off my strong feelings for Alan. But when we were together I generally drank too much, to try to mask what I felt, and whenever I drank too much (and Alan drank too much with me), we usually ended up in a brawl. I hated my shrike-like self-image. It didn't jibe with what I wanted my life to be, so I talked to my shrink about giving up drinking.

"I'm just going to give up booze altogether. That's never been a problem for me."

"No, I don't think you ought to do that. That's the easy way out. It would show far more self-discipline if you would just limit yourself to two drinks, no more."

"That's not possible for me. Whenever I have one drink I just keep going. I'll just have to stop cold."

But I didn't.

As August drew to an end, I was inviting only women friends out to the barn for the last weekends of the season. I just couldn't face another man. I felt physically and emotionally all used up.

Suzie, an old friend from *Vogue*, would love to come. She was depressed over her own love affair with her own married man. Perhaps we could cheer each other up.

On that Friday night I had a toothache, which was only partly relieved by painkillers. Alan hadn't called at all that day. My car was acting up. It was hideously hot in the city and, we heard, in the Hamptons. It was, after all, August. Grim, hot, and depressing August. Suzie and I ate bunless hamburgers and drank wine to shore us up for the two-hour trip which turned out to be a traffic-snarled four-hour nightmare.

Everybody had invited last-ditch houseguests, it seemed, and there was a wild scramble for bed and floor space. I looked at the mass of humanity all over the room and decided to let the bodies fall where they would. I had my wine and painkillers and Valium and Placidyl, and hopes for a bit of Friday-night sleep.

There were parties scheduled everywhere that weekend—cocktail parties, dinner parties, and after-dinner parties—and, for Suzie's sake, I wanted to make them all. My heart wasn't into partying. Neither was my body, which seemed to ache all over. Rather like the tooth. But I kept going, on an inordinate amount of white wine.

On Saturday night, at the last of the party rounds, Suzie got wildly drunk, fell through a door, and passed out. Someone helped me cart her home to her pallet on the floor. I thanked God I could get to bed at a somewhat reasonable hour—2:00 A.M.

At three I was awakened by a searing, piercing pain, right in the middle of my solar plexus. Oh, God! The stomach pains were back.

I took two Fiorinal and two Valium, just in case the "nerves" theory was right, and began to tremble. Here I was, nowhere near my doctor. What would I do if they didn't go away? At six o'clock I took a Percodan.

But the pains got steadily worse and by now they were radiating all around my ribs and into my back. I made some tea, hoping the warmth would help. But it didn't, so I cradled my ribs while the tears slid non-stop down my face until morning.

My housemates were solicitous and worried. I could only writhe and cry out with the pain. It was too hot in the house now so I crawled to the grass outside, where I lay in the sun and prayed. Then I remembered—there was something in my medicine chest I hadn't tried yet, some sample that my doctor had given me long ago, just in case. Talwin. Strong, he'd said. Suzie brought me the tiny beige pill. I swallowed, then finally I slept. When I awoke in the afternoon my stomach was still swollen and tender, but the racking, aching pains were gone. I had several cups of strong coffee to get me in shape for the long, bumper-to-bumper trip back to the city.

Poor Suzie, I thought. Her weekend hadn't been so wonderful. She never got a chance to see the Beautiful People in our beautiful barn. Nobody had looked beautiful at all.

The next morning I telephoned my doctor to tell him about the stomach attack. All he said was, "But we know it isn't anything serious."

And I, of course, never connected the pain with the wine of the night before.

15.

Summer was drawing to a close, and I was almost glad to see it go. For one thing, I was physically exhausted. Those long trips back and forth on the crowded expressway seemed ever more grim. The tensions that had built up throughout the compound were getting on my nerves. And then there was the weather. Hot, sticky, oppressive, it merely added to the explosive undercurrent that flowed, electrically, through the steamy August air.

In our house we had lived an armed truce, ever since Mark and Nils had traded blows over an argument between Greta and the newest blonde. The lawyers, on the verge of a split, had gone back to the city. The sculptor and her beach-boy lover had quarreled, and he was sleeping on his surfboard at the beach. Frannie, exhausted by the hordes of sun-hungry house guests, hung out with me in our house as we tried to keep everything on a temperate, even keel until September. It was a trying, strained time. But we were going to see it through, no matter what, and we'd give our Labor Day party just the way we'd planned.

But it didn't go the way we'd planned. It went like this:

On Friday night, Nils and I got roaring drunk and I got zapped in the eye by the refrigerator door. We laughed crazily as my eye swelled up into an enormous, painful mouse.

I spent Saturday alternately vomiting and holding ice bags to the ugly, bruised lump that had been my eye, while the rest of the crowd went to the beach.

Saturday night I was supposed to play chef. Instead I lay in bed, dressed in my party gear, with waves of nausea sweeping over me. I took Dramamine for the nausea and Fiorinal and a little wine for the pain. The party went roaring on outside my bedroom door.

By midnight there was an uproar. The dish-throwing couple from down the road were screaming obscenities at the sculptor. Someone was screaming back.

I peered from my door and saw it clearly. One more good old Saturday-night crowd of drunk and stoned freaks. I was sick of it all. I wanted to go home, right then, to the calm, quiet, peaceful, safe city.

I would come back later for my clothes. Much later. Like in October.

16.

I couldn't figure out why summer hadn't given me what I'd wanted. I'd had the beautiful house in the most beautiful Hampton with the Beautiful People, but none of us had come away from the experience knowing what to do about our lives. Perhaps autumn in the city would get us back down to the business of sober, serious life.

I threw myself into my work with renewed enthusiasm and vowed to produce the best fashion stories I could under the new restrictions ("no expensive models, no serious expressions, no outrageous clothes"). My first story was to be a picture essay on polyester.

Geoffrey came back from his travels, but, somehow, without his tennis whites and his tan, he didn't look quite as handsome. Although we saw each other a couple of times a week and Geoffrey still claimed to love me, it really didn't seem to matter much. I thought more about Alan than about Geoffrey, and I saw Alan as often as I saw Geoffrey. But Alan didn't claim to love me, although we often made love.

Twice a week I talked with my shrink about Geoffrey and Alan, but we never seemed to come to any conclusions. He just gave me pre-

scriptions for Valium and Placidyl so that at least I could keep relatively calm and get some sleep.

Alan, his friends told me, was in love with someone else. (My heart
leaped up inside my chest and thundered angrily against my ribs. Had I
lost him at last? Was it all over?)

I didn't believe them. Alan had said he loved me. He would tell me it
wasn't true. Friends could be vicious sometimes. They had even told me
how she looked. She looked good, they said. No, I couldn't trust so-
called friends like that. I'd just ask Alan. He'd say it was all lies. (The
thunder in my breast boomed away.)

We met in our favorite little Greek restaurant, over a martini for
Alan, a glass of retsina for me. I thought it expedient to fortify myself
with a bit of wine before I heard the truth—whatever it was—from Alan.
Anyway, I had already fortified myself with a Valium, to quiet the
thunder and ease the galloping nerves down in my stomach. I didn't
want Alan to see how frantic I felt.

Yes, Alan told me, he was involved. In love? Well . . . more or less.
(My hand shook as I drained the glass of wine and ordered another.)
She was twenty-one, blonde, slender, and the most beautiful thing he'd
ever seen. (I drained another glass of wine and held my shaking hands
under the table.) Then Alan's lip curled a little in that evil kind of grin
he had and he looked into his drink and said, "I have to admit, though,
there's one thing that kind of gets to me. She's got needle tracks." A
junkie? Alan had fallen in love with a young, blonde, slender, beautiful
junkie?

I excused myself and went to the telephone to call the office. "I'm
not coming back," I told them. "I'm getting one of my lousy migraines."

"I'll drop you off," Alan said. That tiny sneer of a smile played
across his mouth again.

I held back the tears until I was safely inside my apartment. I held
back the tears until I could go into the kitchen, open the refrigerator
door, and take out the iced bottle of vodka. I had to hold back the
tears. If I didn't, I felt sure I would die. Die of grief. Die of pain. Die of
want. Die of hurt. Just die. I had to hold back the tears just a little bit
longer. Until I could get drunk. God, if I could just be drunk then I
wouldn't feel. Just let the tears wait a minute longer.

I locked the door, turned off the telephone, and poured a big glass of
vodka. When it was gone, I poured another.

From somewhere within the room came a little cry of pain. Like a wounded animal. The sound grew until it filled the room—a whimper, a cry, a moan. It came from me. Tears came in convulsing, gasping sobs. Alan was gone. He would never come back. He was gone forever. He didn't love me. He had never loved me. He loved her.

I drowned in the tears. Tears that were not only for Alan, but for all the world, which didn't love me, had never loved me, would never love me. The world that loved only young, beautiful, slender blondes. Not me.

Like photo slides flashing across my brain came images of Alan and the girl. Alan holding her, Alan kissing her, Alan making love to her. I worried the images like a sore tooth, my mind boring into the pain.

When I awoke it was dark. I must have dozed off. I reached for the bottle of vodka, but it was almost gone. The half-full bottle of Scotch in the liquor cabinet would do. I took a long swig from the bottle. And then another. Until the Scotch was gone.

When I looked at the clock it was two-thirty. I wasn't sure whether it was afternoon or morning. I wasn't sure why I was lying on my bed, still in the same clothes I had put on that morning. I didn't feel so hot. In fact, I felt very, very sick. I was going to throw up. I tried to get up but fell back onto the bed. Holding my hand across my mouth, I grabbed a chair and slowly pulled myself up. I lurched toward the bathroom, but I didn't make it. With an enormous heave, I vomited onto the floor, and at the same moment I fell. The force of the fall sent a table smashing down, showering me with all the precious little objects I'd arranged so painstakingly: mirrors and pictures and lamps and vases, all broken into thousands of tiny pieces. My hand was cut and bleeding badly. I crawled into the bathroom on my hands and knees and coughed up what looked like my entire stomach, this time into the toilet bowl. For what seemed an eternity I retched and heaved and threw up while my hair, soaked with sweat and vomit, trailed in the dirty water. There was vomit all over the floor, all over the walls, all over me.

When, at last, it seemed over, I weakly pulled myself up. The face in the mirror looked at me with eyes swollen nearly shut in a ghostly pale mass of puffed and distorted flesh. It was a drunk. It was me.

I had to get back to bed. I cleaned the filth from my clothes and tried, in vain, to wipe it from the walls. I just didn't have the strength. Tomorrow. Just let me get to bed now. I did not wake again until noon.

There was no question of my going to work. There was no question of anyone's not believing I was sick. "I don't know when I'll be in," I told them.

When I could finally get out of bed, I made my way through the dried-out mess on the floor into the bathroom. I needed to wash my face, open my eyes a little. But I couldn't recognize the person looking back at me from the mirror. There were dark blue circles under my half-closed eyes. My eyelids were obscenely and ludicrously frog-swollen. Lines were carved deeply into my ashen skin. I looked every bit as sick as I felt. As I was.

I couldn't afford to think about Alan. If I thought about Alan with. . . . No, I couldn't think. Otherwise, it would begin all over again. Not a drink. God! Sickening to think of it. I'd make some tea. And what else? Some vitamin B (I took three capsules) and an antihistamine and something for my headache. (I took two Fiorinal and two aspirin.) And perhaps a Dramamine for this god-awful nausea. And tea and toast. Ah, that was better.

But my nerves felt rubbed raw. I took two Valium and went back to sleep.

In the afternoon I took two more vitamin B's, two more Fiorinal, and two more Valium. And I went back to sleep again.

In the evening I drank some soup and tried to clean up the house. Oh, Lord, it makes me so sick. Not just the mess on the floor. The mess inside me, that would make me do a thing like this.

That night I didn't take a drink. I took a Placidyl, a Fiorinal, and a Valium. And I slept soundly. At last.

For the next couple of months, my life bobbed up and down. Geoffrey came back from another trip, but our sizzling romance seemed fizzled. We agreed that it was pointless to continue our semi-affair, and parted without much ado. A month later I heard that Geoffrey was planning to marry a divorcée from back-bay Boston. "She wears circle pins," mutual friends told me.

Alan, on the other hand, continued to call. Oh, he was still seeing the beautiful, slender, blonde young junkie, but he wanted to see me as well. (He missed me, he said.) I don't know why I let him, but I did.

17.

I had continued for a year on my diet doctor's regimen, which consisted of plenty of protein in the form of great big steaks and cheese and plenty of fat in the form of butter and bacon. I laughingly said that if cholesterol killed me, then at least the corpse would look good, because my body had never looked better. On the outside. On the inside, strange things were happening.

My stomach pains came more often and more severely now, incapacitating me. But no matter how often I questioned my doctor, the answer was always the same—either "It's gas" or "It's nerves." Both answers made me furious. It was as if he were accusing me of malingering, I fumed. And there seemed to be no suggestions other than Percodan—and Valium, just in case it turned out to be nerves after all.

And I was still getting migraines. I had Fiorinal for those, and when it didn't do the trick I could always resort to Percodan.

But I just never seemed to feel well at all, and in my medicine cabinet there was a growing assortment of bottles. There were little tablets for the diarrhea that often came the morning after a big party, big tablets for gas pains, just in case that really was what my stomach problem was all about. There were oddments such as aromatic spirits of ammonia—one of those nerve potions my grandmother used to depend on—and paregoric, left over from some previously uncontrollable bout with diarrhea. Of course I knew that paregoric contained opium and so I kept it around (even though its age was uncertain) in case I needed a really strong painkiller some day. My Valium now came in bottles of a hundred. It gave me a certain sense of security to see them there in a nice, yellow-packed, substantially sized vial. I knew, of course, that my Valium prescriptions were refillable. My doctor had said he knew I'd never be addicted; I just wasn't the type. That's why he trusted me with refills. And there was Placidyl, but the capsules weren't blood-red anymore. They were murky green now. Somewhere along the way, Placidyl stopped keeping me asleep for eight hours. When I complained to my shrink, he changed my prescription to something stronger. The new, bigger, dark-green Placidyl capsules were the 750-milligram size. Of course I kept the 500s, as well.

Besides these, there were assorted nasal sprays and sinus decongestants, coated aspirin (so as not to irritate my tender stomach), antihistamines, Dramamine for nausea (ergo for hangovers) and vitamins of every description. It was becoming difficult to close the cabinet door.

After that summer of '70, we of the country-compound gave parties on through fall and into winter, as if trying to hold on to something precious. I really wasn't sure just what. Surely not summer. Our parties were usually raucous, and once or twice I went home with one man, completely forgetting I had come with another. And I got very, very high at almost every party. It took my mind off Alan.

Hot pants came and went and midiskirts came and stayed, and we tried them all. I don't remember much about the music, but I do know that we didn't dance.

Janis Joplin died from drugs. So did Jimi Hendrix. Warhol superstar Edie Sedgwick was dead; others were non compos mentis. My beautiful hairdresser, Nigel, had seemingly lost his rational mind to LSD. The ranks, it seemed, were thinning.

I was invited to an Easter luncheon with our lawyer friends from the country. But by lunchtime, they both lay dead, smashed into pieces when their car careened into a barrier on the FDR Drive. They had been drinking heavily, their friends said. Their bodies had been robbed, even as they lay in the road. We all trooped off together (for courage) to a depressing, crowded funeral. It was not, so far, a very good year.

18.

We rolled uneasily into another summer. It seemed like no time since barn time, and yet here the beach season was, all over again, brand new. But none of us knew, yet, what we wanted to do with it. Nobody wanted to get stuck in town, but nobody organized anything either. At the last minute, Frannie opted for a house in Southampton—a nice, big house that would hold us all as houseguests. It sounded like a good idea to me—I could get a tan, and have no responsibilities. I greedily accepted the invitation.

But somehow, that year, I didn't feel quite ready to enter into the frenzied fun of another Hampton summer. I felt quiet, as if I were waiting for something to happen. Surely, something would, one day, happen to my life.

Much of my life, including weekends, was given over to weeping about Alan. We were seeing each other relatively often, and when we saw each other, we made love. But there was no more talk of being in love. The beautiful young junkie was gone, reclaimed by her ex-lover, who had been sprung from jail. But, though I had no proof at all, I felt sure Alan was sleeping with someone else. As well as his wife. And me.

And when he left me, the elation I had felt in bed became, instead, deep depression.

I maintained my equilibrium with a combination of vitamins and Valium. Placidyl put me to sleep and caffeine woke me up. "If I could just shoot coffee into my veins," I said jokingly, "life would be so much simpler."

Everyone in the Hamptons that summer was experimenting with cocaine, but I still lived with childhood impressions of dope addicts who were hooked on the white powder, and I saw cocaine on a par with heroin. I politely declined to snort the stuff.

As a matter of fact, I just couldn't get my act together for summer. We all lay in the sun and usually didn't even bother to go to the beach, which was farther away in Southampton and less inviting. We still drank wine spritzers, but my stomach always felt lousy afterward. Everybody seemed just a wee bit down. And soon it was Labor Day again and, again, everybody seemed rather glad. I desperately wanted to get back to town to see what I might do about my life.

But it seemed that there was *nothing* to do about my life. My work load was, by now, monumental, physically exhausting, and frustrating. I found myself growing more irritable all the time.

At night I invariably hit the refrigerator for the booze before I took off my coat. And now, in the morning, I hit the refrigerator for a slug of booze before I put on my coat. To get me going, I told myself.

I still had my shape, but other things weren't looking so hot. My hair was thin and unhealthy-looking. So were my nails. They were perpetually breaking off to the quick. Not only were they ugly; they were painful. I wondered whether it might be something I wasn't eating.

I was going home for Christmas, and I informed the diet doctor that I was going to eat every good thing my mother could cook up. I was sick and tired of fat and protein. What I needed was one good Southern biscuit. That ought to fix me up. I'd come in to be checked out when I returned.

And I did exactly that. The peculiar thing was that, in the week I was home eating whatever I chose, my fingernails began to grow back. I was sure it was the biscuits. That's why I had craved bread! My body must be needing it somehow.

But when I got back to New York, the diet doctor said, "Nonsense!" I went back to the no-carbohydrate diet and my shape stayed good. So, for a time, did my nails.

Other strange things were happening, though—little annoying aches and pains, odd illnesses I'd never experienced before. For example, recurring bouts of cystitis, a painful bladder infection. We'd have to do a cystoscope to see what was going on.

People kept telling me how painful the procedure was, and the more they said that, the more scared I got. Lord, I knew I couldn't take a lot of pain. I never could. I tried not to think about it as the appointment loomed nearer.

My appointment with the urologist was for eleven o'clock in the morning. At ten-thirty I decided it would be prudent to take a Valium. Then I decided this was definitely a two-Valium morning. And then I thought, God, why don't I take a painkiller now? If it's going to be that bad, maybe I can deaden my body a little bit beforehand. I swallowed two Fiorinal and telephoned my doctor's office. When I told the nurse what I'd taken she said, "Well, I hope you get there!"

I was simply amazed that the examination didn't hurt at all. Could *this* be what everybody had said was so painful? The urologist assured me it was his gentle hands. But I made a mental note that the thing to do was always to take the painkillers first. That way I could avoid pain forever.

I was going to need an operation. (Shivers skittered up my spine.) An operation? Me? Nothing serious. Just a biopsy. General anesthesia and two days in the hospital. That's all.

Couldn't we please do it without the general anesthetic? It terrifies me! No, not this time.

When I got home I swallowed two more Valium to steady my shaking hands and calm my churning stomach.

What is wrong with the medical profession? I wondered. They really must not have the answers. If they had, then I wouldn't be in this physical fix.

I thought I'd start doing some research myself, to see what this bladder business was all about. Adelle Davis ought to have something to say. I had her book somewhere.

Over the next two weeks I read every health book I could get my hands on, marking passages from "bladder" to "pain." I was willing to try all the recommended "cures," from calcium for pain to vitamin A for bladder to vitamin B to calm my shaky nerves. It would be far healthier, I reasoned, to stay calm on vitamins than on Valium. I was going to try for a health turnaround. Maybe I'd even try to get off my diet merry-go-round.

I checked into the hospital on the first day of spring and hoped that I'd be all healed by Easter, which was only two weeks away. In my little silver pillbox I had a supply of Valium and Fiorinal and Placidyl. I wanted to try to stay asleep right up to the hour of the operation.

In what seemed seconds since the anesthesiologist had said, "This won't hurt, Miss Crenshaw," I heard her saying, "It's all over. Wake up." I murmured "I'm going to throw up," and the anesthesiologist replied, "Nobody throws up on this anesthetic." I vomited all over her shoes.

I vomited for twelve hours straight. My roommates said they had never seen anybody that sick. My doctor said he'd never seen anyone throw up from that anesthetic. Nobody ever dreamed it could be the Valium I hadn't gotten that day. Nobody ever dreamed it could be drug withdrawal.

I left the hospital twenty-four hours later, on a Saturday. Late that night the urologist telephoned to say the biopsy had been fine. When I told him I hadn't been worried, he said, "Why not? It might have been cancer, you know." I took two Valium and a Placidyl and went to sleep, at last, in my own bed.

19.

The fashion business in the early seventies was in the midst of some sort of schizophrenic freak-out. Half of the professional "fashion ladies" were wearing gypsy rags and babushkas, while the other half wore pants. I had opted for blue jeans as a kind of nose-thumbing gesture at the whole thing. I really just couldn't take it seriously anymore. Fashion, that is. It all seemed so silly.

Instead, I elected to do articles on beauty and health, and the more I got involved in those, the less important fashion seemed. And the more I got involved in the health business, the more convinced I became that the answer to all medical problems lay in the right kind of diet and the right kinds of vitamins. I tested every theory on myself, of course, and it did seem to be working.

In a short time I told my diet doctor that I really didn't want to continue anymore with his no-carbohydrate way of eating. I just plain didn't think it was healthy. Anyway, I was beginning to gain weight on his bloody diet and *that* certainly wasn't normal. And although he'd kept me on zero carbohydrates for what I thought was far too long, he still hadn't been able to hold back the steady climb of the scales which had, by now, gone back up to 110. Well, since I was no longer losing but seemed to be gaining weight and since the queer sort of diet didn't seem healthy to a newly health-conscious me, then I would leave him and devise my own diet—a low-calorie one. It would be far healthier in the long run, I was sure, and I knew it would work. I wanted to get those pounds down to 100, and then I'd stop. Anyway, I'd let him hear. I left his office to embark on my 1000-calorie-diet life—with me as supervising physician.

Alan and I were still lunching a lot, but we talked mostly about business—both his and mine. There didn't seem to be much personal stuff to discuss. We knew what the situation was. During the day we saw each other and at night he went home to his wife. Happily, I said. Miserably, he said.

Our relationship was calmer, somehow. I attributed it to the fact that I always swallowed some Valium before I met him.

My drinking, oddly enough, seemed to have increased. I was drinking half a bottle of vodka per night by now, and the odd thing was I didn't really know why. It wasn't because I was miserable over Alan. This time I seemed to really want to get drunk. It meant getting away from it all: deadlines and stories and typing and research. It meant peace and quiet.

I still threw up whenever I drank a lot, but by now I got the signals in time to make it to the toilet. I had grown accustomed to hanging my head over the toilet.

My hangovers were, of course, horrendous, but I knew enough to take massive amounts of vitamin B, antihistamine, Valium, and Fiorinal, plus a nasal decongestant. That usually got me going in the morning. That and another slug of vodka—to calm my nerves.

I decided to write a book. For one thing, I could never find the answers to my own nutrition-and-beauty questions in any of the books I read. I rationalized that if I needed (and couldn't find) that information, then there must be a lot of other people in the same boat. The answer, of course, would be for me to do the definitive book on health and beauty.

I discussed my idea with Alan over lunch. "I think it could make a lot of money," he said firmly.

Within a week I had an outline, and a week after submitting it to a publisher, I had sold the book. *I had sold my very first book!*

Alan and I rushed out to celebrate. I was, all at once, elated, excited, hopeful, and scared.

Alan was surprisingly supportive. "You can do it. You'll be fine." But I wondered whether I'd really have the nerve, after all. One thing was crystal clear—I was going to have to change my way of drinking if the book were ever to materialize. If I didn't, fear would probably keep me drunk until deadline time.

I simply had to produce the book. It would be my ticket out of the *New York Times*.

I told my friends I thought I might be an alcoholic, but they merely scoffed. My shrink repeated that I just needed to limit myself to one or two drinks. Alan thought the whole idea was nonsense. Only my father said he thought perhaps I ought to try AA.

I went to a single AA meeting, in a dingy church basement room on the Upper East Side, where I listened to a dreary-looking man tell a depressing story about his own alcoholism. I escaped the place as quickly as possible and vowed that, if I was going to stop drinking, then I would just stop, period. Why get depressed about it?

I was going to sign the book contract in April, on my birthday. It wasn't planned that way; it just happened. A little bit of birthday lagniappe. The night before, Alan and I celebrated. I got very drunk, he got very drunk, and we made very beautiful love.

My birthday hangover was anything but beautiful, but I took all my hangover remedies and, remarkably, got to the publisher's office on time. He had a surprise, he said—a celebratory bottle of champagne! It would, I decided, be my very last drink. We toasted each other, we both signed the contract, and my life, at that moment, shifted into another gear.

I became an author.

I gave up booze.

It never even occurred to me to give up pills.

At work the next day I announced loudly that I had given up drinking. A lot of my co-workers laughed, and some said, "I think that's great," and one said, "Oh, Mary Ann, come on!" But I had taken my last drink, all right. At least for a very long time.

As in the past, I didn't miss drinking at all. On the contrary, I felt a hell of a lot better without it. I thanked God for Valium, which kept me calm with none of alcohol's destructive side effects: no hangovers, no vomiting, no outrageous behavior, no awful scenes. God knows, I was sick of all that. If I wanted to get high with the gang, I could always smoke a little grass. But I really wasn't interested in getting high. I was interested in keeping calm. And for that I would take Valium. After all, Valium couldn't hurt me. Booze could and would kill me. I was, I reminded myself, really an alcoholic.

For the next six months I worked harder than ever before. All summer long I incarcerated myself in my apartment to do research, heroically turning down every single weekend invitation and, for the first time, never once exposing myself to the soothing, calming, tanning sun.

My friends were grumpy. "You can't be working *all* the time," they complained. But I was.

My responsibilities at the paper seemed to grow even heavier as more people, unhappy with the newest regimen there, were leaving. They were never, it seemed, replaced, and those of us who were left took up the slack. We were bombarded with more and more memos outlining more and more stringent rules for our department to follow. We were beginning to get the picture that the fashion department was the newspaper's stepchild—nobody's favorite baby.

My cohorts in the fashion department (those who were still left) talked more and more about leaving, but I couldn't leave yet. I needed my job, at least until I had finished the book and made my name and my fortune. So I bowed before the new and more-difficult-to-follow rules and regulations and did my best to please our unpleasant boss. While my co-workers fought for their right to show avant-garde fashion, I photographed shirt-dresses on insipid-looking models. Because the boss always said, *"Smile,* Mary Ann, they have to *smile,"* my models always looked like beautifully made-up hyenas. What did I care? Just let the layouts be approved so I could get on to the next thing. When the book was done, I'd get out altogether. I just prayed I could hang on that long.

I still went with Erica for drinks to our little *Times*-neighborhood restaurant. She had wine and I had double orders of strong Greek coffee. So many, in fact, that the owner often said, jokingly, "I'm sorry, madame, I don't think we can serve you any more." And we all laughed.

A lot of my favorite bartenders, in fact, were impressed with the fact that I'd given up booze. Some even asked me how I'd managed. I always told them I'd just stopped. Good willpower.

No matter how tired I was when I got home, I had to work on my book. I worked until two or three in the morning, and every weekend, all weekend long. I was going to make sure that it was the most comprehensive, accurate, and well-researched book in its field. I kept reading and learning and filing my notes for six long months.

I told my shrink I didn't think I needed him anymore. My life seemed under control. Alan and I were getting along beautifully, now that I no longer badgered him about marriage. (I was far too busy to think about *that*.) And with his counsel and encouragement, I felt elated and confident that I was going to be able to make the book a success. When that happened, my life would be absolutely where I wanted it to be. Together. Perfect.

To my surprise, my shrink agreed, "But I'll always be here if you ever want to come back."

I was learning an awful lot about what constituted good nutrition while having a wonderful time eating all the good things that had been so long denied me by the diet doctor—like bread, fruits and vegetables, even pasta. I was having no problem at all keeping the calories to one thousand a day, now that I wasn't drinking. I told everyone it was simply a matter of willpower. Anyone who set his mind to it could do what I was doing. And I watched delightedly as the scale needle once again began to go down. I was determined to see whether, by using my own diet methods, I could get down to my ideal weight of 100 pounds. I had a good start. I was already looking nice and slim. "Skinny," Erica told me. I didn't agree.

While I was adding up the calories in a notebook each day, I was also experimenting with other things—vitamins, minerals, herbs. I knew that as long as I limited my food intake so drastically, I'd really better supplement my diet with megadoses of vitamins and minerals. I haunted the health food stores and, by trial and error, developed a regimen of food supplements that would give me the top-notch nutritional program I wanted to have. I was going to be living proof of the theory that beauty is as beauty eats. My hair was growing beautifully—shoulder length, shiny and healthy. My skin was luminous and clear—people commented on it and asked me my secret. I was terribly encouraged by that, and continued to read more and experiment more with all of those fascinating food supplements that helped round out my 1000 calories.

By the end of summer I was pulling in my belt another notch every week and men friends were patting me on the seat of my nearly empty jeans and saying things like, "Gotta fill that up a little. You're losing your nice rear end." I always laughed and secretly felt very, very flattered.

My super-health regimen should have had me *feeling* wonderful, but, in fact, the stomach pains seemed to be getting worse. And the more nervous I got about the approaching book deadline, the more acute they were. I was beginning to believe it might be nerves after all.

My doctor suggested we try Librax, a turquoise capsule that contained some Librium and was intended specifically to relax the stomach. I added it to my pillbox and prayed it would help.

By autumn I weighed 103 pounds and the truth was, I didn't look well at all. Friends kept saying, "Don't lose any more weight. You're too thin already." And, although I was still determined to reach my hundred-pound goal, I realized that all the work at the *Times* plus the book must have gotten me a little run-down. I resolved to step up my already large doses of vitamins. I took all the B-vitamins separately, in megadoses. I took 50,000 units of vitamin A per day, vitamin D, vitamin E, brewer's yeast, liver, and virtually anything else that anybody suggested might be healthful. I was determined to show the world that food and food supplements could do what medicine couldn't—cure all ills.

But I was feeling more and more tired all the time.

One Sunday morning at three I was awakened by gripping, sharp pains in my stomach. I became panicky. If only my doctor were in town —what would he do? I had to do something. I had to *do* something. There was only one thing I could think of to do—take something—anything—that might help.

I took everything. Two Percodan, two Librax, even two Valium (just in case it *was* nerves). Eventually the pain subsided and I was able to sleep.

On Monday morning, I telephoned my doctor. When I told him what I had done, he said, "You did exactly the right thing." But what did he think it was, for God's sake? "I don't know. Let's see what happens." What would happen, of course, would be serious indeed.

Late in October New York experienced a hurricane with eighty-five-mile-an-hour winds and rains that backed water up to knee-height in the streets. Where was I? Photographing winter-white dresses at Lincoln

Center, while the winds rippled the big glass panes in Avery Fisher Hall. We all laughed at the amazement on the tourists' faces as they gathered to watch us. "Rushing the season, aren't you?" they asked. When we'd finished, we pulled on our boots and waded through the streams across Broadway. It took me one hour and a seven-dollar cab fare to get from West Sixty-fifth Street to East Seventy-fourth.

The following day I awoke with a sore throat and a high fever. Everything hurt, in fact. My head, my body, my stomach. Not those hideous stomach pains, but the sort that come with flu. That was what I had, all right, the flu. Damn! I didn't need that. But it was going around. I took a couple of Fiorinal to ease all the aches and telephoned the office to say I wouldn't make it in for a few days. Who, they wanted to know, would be doing my work? I really didn't know. I'd do what I could by phone.

I took the antibiotics for the bug and plenty of Fiorinal plus aspirin to keep the pain down, and Valium, now and again, to help me sleep a bit. But I continued to feel terrible, and by the end of a week I was no better at all.

A full two weeks had passed before the fever subsided and I could return to work. I looked, I thought, like death. My face was pale, thin, haggard, and little red spots burned in my cheeks. Everybody said, "Lord! you've gotten much too thin." I really didn't know just what was wrong with me.

We were headed toward Christmas, and everyone in the office was busy trying to find exciting stories to fill those weeks. I felt jittery and tense, and for the very first time since I stopped drinking, longed for just one glass of wine. But I knew I couldn't have that. I took a Valium, instead, whenever the tension got too great. I knew I had to keep calm to avoid any recurrence of the stomach pains, or the migraines, which still came regularly. At the very first twinge of any impending pain, I dived for my pillbox and took Valium, Fiorinal, and Librax. They were my three stooges, the triumvirate. They were what was keeping me on my feet. I felt quite sure of that.

After a week at the office, I developed a fever again. My doctor ordered me back into bed, back onto antibiotics. I took more aspirin, and more Fiorinal to relieve the aches and pains in my head and body.

Oh God, not again! It was happening—the swelling in my stomach, the aching, the pain. I sat in bed and rocked back and forth while the tears streamed down my cheeks. Nothing helped. I took all the medicine. Nothing helped at all. I kept taking Fiorinal and Valium and aspirin and Librax every two hours. After a while I resorted to Percodan. And then I remembered the Talwin—there was another tablet in that little sample packet. I swallowed that, and, little by little, the pains ceased and then finally went away. I fell into a deep, exhausted sleep.

The next morning I telephoned my doctor once more. This time I was angry and determined. This was going to be the last time I ever made such a call, because this time we were going to find some answer. I didn't give a damn *how* many doctors I might have to consult.

"I just can't take this anymore. I'm coming in to see you, and I'm not leaving until we've found out what's wrong with me. I can't stand the pain anymore."

"That might take a long time."

"I have plenty of time."

"Well, describe the pain to me again."

I launched into my thousandth description of the stomach pains, the sharp pain in the solar plexus, the radiation of pain around the ribs, the ache in my back.

This time my doctor did not say, "It's your nerves." He said, "It sounds like it could be the pancreas. Come in this afternoon and we'll get some blood."

For the first time, I began to hope.

After taking six vials of blood and some careful pokes at my stomach, my doctor sent me home to wait for the lab report. At ten o'clock that night my telephone rang. My doctor said, "Mary Ann, it certainly wasn't your nerves. It was acute pancreatitis. It's lucky we found it when we did."

I felt a tightening around my heart. I had no idea at all what it meant.

"I've discussed it with the gastroenterology department at the hospital. Here's what we think we have to do."

Pancreatitis, he explained, is an inflammation of the pancreas. It means the pancreas can no longer digest protein. (Could it have been that damned low-carbohydrate diet? I asked myself.) The inflammation was severe—acute, in fact—and dangerous. I was to stay in bed and he would send me a prescription for some pills I was to take. The hospital thought they should be taken before, during, and after meals as an emergency measure. My doctor had decided three times a day, after meals, would do. They were called Kanulase and were pancreas enzyme plus a little hydrochloric acid. They should be able to heal my damaged pancreas. We wouldn't try hospitalization yet.

"I think you ought to tell your family, Mary Ann, and have them call me," said my doctor. "You're not going to be able to work for a while. I'll call the *Times* tomorrow. We're going to have to arrange a medical leave. I'll take care of it. Oh, one other thing—make sure you don't take anything to drink. You know, any alcohol. You won't be able to do that again." I reminded my doctor that I had already given up booze.

But what my doctor didn't say was that acute pancreatitis can result from heavy drinking. Nobody mentioned that until much, much later.

I didn't go into the office again. A leave of absence was arranged between my doctor and the *Times*'s medical department. I would have three months in which to recover. I was going to have to stay in bed for a while.

My mother was frantic and wanted to come to New York. I dissuaded her, saying that I was in good hands and assuring her I would be all right. Alan telephoned every day and seemed genuinely concerned, though he didn't visit often. I reasoned I wasn't very good company just now, and, anyway, I felt too sick. Erica called every day, too, and kept me abreast of all the gossip from the office. I had the feeling that the bosses weren't quite sure whether I was really as sick as I said. I didn't care. I felt too awful to care what they thought. *I* knew I couldn't get out of bed at all.

In fact, I continued to feel worse. The pains came regularly—they never seemed to go away—and I felt weak and exhausted all the time.

My doctor sent me to a radiologist for another series of X-rays. We'd start with the upper GI tract, the less disagreeable. Just drink a bit of barium, etc. A solicitous, pretty little nurse brought me the barium. "Here, drink it all, now. It isn't so bad." It was horrible, but I sucked it through the straw until it was all down.

As the nurse bustled about lining me up on the table, I knew, with dead certainty, that the barium was now going to come up. "I'm going to throw up." "No, you can't. You may feel that way but barium's too heavy to come up." I just made it into the bathroom; the barium came up into the sink.

Everybody was a bit perturbed. That wasn't supposed to happen.

Well, I'd just have to drink it all over again. We did have to get the X-rays.

The vomiting continued through four doses of barium. I was lying on the floor of the dressing room now, shivering and weak. The puzzled technologists summoned the radiologist. "Well," he told me, "I'm going to give you some peppermint-flavored stuff. I don't like to use it, because the pictures aren't as clear. But maybe it won't nauseate you quite as much. Let's try, anyway, shall we?" I drank it, and could almost feel it starting from way down in my stomach and crawling all the way back up into my throat. When I looked down into the sink, I saw I hadn't just thrown up barium. The sink was filled with bright red stuff. Blood. My blood. From my stomach.

I managed to make myself heard, calling the radiologist's name. He looked at the stuff in the sink, then took my arm and helped me back into the X-ray room. "We've got to get some pictures," he said grimly. "Don't worry too much. That's perfectly normal. Just an irritation, that's all." I was scared. Throwing up blood was what you did when you were dying. Was I dying?

"It may be normal to him," my doctor was saying, "but it certainly isn't normal to me. Mary Ann, I believe you need to be with your family. They can take care of you, and I don't want you alone right now. Let's just say I'm sending you home." What he didn't say was that he was sending me home, perhaps to die. Though he said it to my family.

It was mid-November, and some of the rushing-the-season Christmas lights were already up in midtown. I felt as if I'd stepped from some time capsule into a season I hadn't seen coming. I hadn't left my apartment for nearly a month, except for the one trip to the radiologist's office. An entire autumn had passed me by. Well, I'd worry about Christmas when I got home. There were things I had to do first.

I farmed out my plants to a neighbor and arranged for the post office to forward my mail. Alan came to say goodbye, but didn't stay long. There really wasn't much to say, and I just wasn't able to make love. So he held me tightly while I fretted. "What am I going to do about the book?"

"Don't worry. It'll be here when you get back."

Neither of us knew when I'd get back.

That night, when I stepped on the bathroom scale, it read 97 pounds.

I flew into my hometown on the day before Thanksgiving, and the long siege began. My childhood doctor was going to look after me. He wanted to do some lab tests to confirm those done in New York. Meanwhile, I was to rest.

"But I can't rest," I told him. "I've got work to do. I have a book to write."

"Mary Ann, there are only two things you can do. You can go back to New York and write the book and die. Or you can stay here and do as I tell you and live."

I didn't see that it was much of a choice.

The lab tests confirmed pancreatitis, no longer acute, and my two doctors conferred by long distance on the course of my treatment.

I wouldn't have to be hospitalized—in fact, I didn't have to stay in bed—but I was to sit down all the time. Not only that, I was to eat plenty—the emphasis was on *plenty*—of home-cooked, wholesome food. Of course, I could never touch alcohol again. It would be, beyond doubt, fatal. (I thanked God I'd already given up booze.) I was to leave the house only once per day, to take a ride in the car. Other than that, I was to do absolutely nothing. I was to resign myself to three months of inactivity. Then perhaps—*perhaps*—I would get well.

We celebrated Christmas with a lovely, old-fashioned tree. Somehow home had never looked more beautiful, with the fire burning in the grate and the family all gathered together once again. I'd managed, by telephone and mail, to get some presents under the tree, and it seemed just like the Christmases of my childhood. I was feeling much better now, and I looked healthier. The pallor had left my cheeks and my hair was looking thick and healthy. My fingernails seemed to have grown back for good.

My friends came to visit, and we reminisced about our school days. Friends from the office phoned regularly on the paper's toll-free line and we swapped stories—they about the newest restrictions on the poor little fashion department, I about the Southeast Conference football games. Auburn had knocked the hell out of Alabama that year. Hadn't they heard?

Alan rarely called, but then I called him almost every day. I felt resigned by now to Alan's cool detachment. It was just his way, I told myself. Besides, he was married.

On New Year's Day I watched Alabama lose the Cotton Bowl on television and I fretted about when I could set out for New York. I was concerned about the book. If I didn't get back to it soon, there would be no chance of making the deadline. As for the *Times*—well, I knew I didn't feel up to that yet. I felt weak as a kitten. I would feel weak, they had told me, for a very long time. A year or more.

At the end of six weeks, against all medical advice, I returned to New York. Surely I could at least type a few pages a day.

My friends were all glad to have me back, Alan seemed glad to have me back, and God knows I was glad to be back. Everything seemed more normal once I was back in semi-harness. I felt more sure that everything would be OK.

I began to write, though I could only keep at it for about an hour or so a day. After that, I collapsed into bed. Once a day I left the house to shop for food. The rest of my life was spent sitting down. It was all I felt up to.

On Valentine's Day I went back to work at the *Times*. I was given a desk-bound job, and for the next three months recuperated on company time. When I felt up to it, I worked on my book. A lot of the time I couldn't work for the company or myself. I just gave out.

From time to time, the stomach pains returned. When they did, I took two Fiorinal, a Percodan, two Valium, two Kanulase, and two Librax and went to bed. Within a few hours, the pain always ceased.

I had learned my lesson: If I took all of the medicine at once, the pain would stop sooner. I would not forget that. Besides, my doctor had told me it was the right thing to do.

I didn't stop to think that I had added a few pills since my doctor had said that.

By spring I was back in the swing of things, carrying a full-time reporter's job with all its inherent tensions. Still, it felt good to be back. I began to work on the book once more, and in April turned in the manuscript. The book was good, I thought (Alan agreed), and I felt reasonably sure it was going to be a success.

My health was improving fast. Though I still tired quickly and had to take it easy, I looked human once again, and for the first time in my life I was eating to *gain* weight. That had never happened before and I was enjoying it like mad, eating everything in sight—everything my weight problems had denied me all my life. Like all the pasta and potatoes I could hold. A hundred pounds, after all, had looked pretty scary, so when my weight got back to 104, I decided to let it stay.

I continued to take multiple-vitamin supplements, in megadoses, just to make sure I wouldn't let myself get run down again, and I tried to steer clear of unnecessary stress. Whenever I felt anxious about something, I took Valium. It seemed the better part of valor. I certainly didn't want any return of acute pancreatitis. After all, I'd barely escaped that with my life. We were keeping that under control with the Kanulase three times a day, plus Librax if my stomach began to swell.

My medicine cabinet was, in fact, full up. The prescription drugs plus all the vitamins and minerals made for a hefty lineup of pills.

By summer I felt pretty much back to normal. I was looking healthy again, too. I had my shoulder-length locks cut into a short, chic new shape, bought some new clothes, and decided it was high time I got back into fashion, both the look and the business. I kept myself thin, but not skinny, by doing all the things I'd set forth in the book, from drinking vinegar to taking the right vitamins to eating the right food. A friend asked me what diet I was on, and when I replied, "None," said, "You mean you've conquered fat?" Apparently I had. I was proud that I'd followed all my own health recommendations, even prouder that they'd worked so well.

Throughout the summer I worked on the proofs of the book, and when it finally went off to the printer, I relaxed in the confident belief that the book was going to be a success. Hooray! My life was at last on the right track and I could see where I was going.

The Times shifted leaders once again, and our department was put under a new command. We moved all our belongings to different offices and cautiously settled in to learn this year's rules. Winter found me working harder than ever, producing a story a week instead of one a month. The children's special was still on my shoulders, and the tempo at the office was triple-time. I seemed never to have a moment's breather.

Alan was still very much in the picture of my life, but by now we had reached an entente. We saw each other regularly, for lunch, for dinner, even for parties now and again. Weekends he still devoted to his wife and family. Although Alan claimed to be miserably unhappy in his marriage and was always talking about "when I leave," I had resigned myself to the fact of his always being a married man. I didn't even mind much anymore. I had the best of both possible worlds. Alan said he loved me and made love to me, and when he left me to go to his wife, I had other friends to take up the slack. It was, I decided, a pretty good setup. Anyway, I wasn't so sure marriage was what I had ever wanted. Maybe I would never have the time for that.

At the end of January I slipped on a patch of ice and broke my arm. My doctor said I was damned lucky it hadn't been my neck. I didn't feel so damned lucky. By the time he'd set and then reset the shattered arm, I'd swallowed six Percodan to try to deaden the pain. Everyone was incredulous: "You mean it *still* hurts?" My tolerance for painkillers seemed to have increased mightily, a dangerous sign, indeed. But then nobody bothered to tell me that. Perhaps nobody noticed.

My book was published in February, and I did much of the promotion tour with my arm in a cast. Everything went well, though, and I stayed Valium-calm while I flew from city to city, one day at a time, on a grueling schedule of interviews and television talk shows. Wherever I went I took all of my vitamins and such with me, for I needed all the energy I could muster. At night I always took a Placidyl, to make sure I got the rest I needed and in the morning I woke myself up with plenty of coffee and a jolt of strong vitamin capsules.

By summer I could relax at last. The book had been an enormous success and had made money. We'd sold two hundred thousand copies, and the paperback rights had gone for a six-figure sum. There had been other rewards as well. I felt more secure at the paper now that I knew I had other options. I walked the halls feeling more like an author than a reporter, accepting the congratulations of my peers. My family was ecstatic and mailed me clippings and stories from all the hometown newspapers. (Local girl makes good.) The success felt just wonderful. Wow! This was what I was meant to do with my life! I had set out to make a name for myself, and, by George, I'd done it.

There were, of course, complications that came with the money, and I felt more than a bit nervous about those. I spent a lot of time conferring with my lawyer and with Alan, trying to decide the wisest investments to make, trying to choose between real estate and the stock market. My Katie Scarlett O'Hara heritage won out, and I decided to buy an apartment. After all, I needed a lot more room now that I was a real working author. The little Seventy-fourth Street apartment I'd loved for so long was knee-deep in paper. I began the long search for just the right apartment. It had to be big, it had to be cheerful, and it had to look like a home.

The moment I entered the apartment I knew I'd found the place. A large foyer opened onto a living room of magnificent proportions. The room was a soft yellow with white-shuttered windows and glorious woodwork. There was a fireplace at one end of the room, and the ceilings were at least sixteen feet high. Geraniums bloomed in window boxes outside the four long windows, and the view to the north looked out over gardens and church spires that could have been in Paris instead of New York. The light changed with the passing clouds, turning the walls from buttercup to gold. I was enchanted. It was not an apartment—it was a home. I knew I had to have it. Best of all, it was just two blocks away. I could still have my old friendly neighborhood.

"It's too expensive," my lawyer said. "I don't care," I replied. I rationalized that it would all work out on the tax end of things. After all, it would be my office as well as my home. I pointed out the investment potential in an apartment that size (two spacious bedrooms, two baths, maid's room, enormous kitchen, pantry). If I ever wanted to sell, there'd be no chance at all of not recouping the price. On the contrary, I'd stand to make a lot. And, while I knew the place needed work, I didn't have to do that all at once. I had plenty of time.

In October I moved. There was a hard lump somewhere around my heart when I realized that I was leaving my happy little apartment for good. Oh well, I thought, things will be even better in the new place. But a small voice from deep inside of me said, "Suppose they aren't?"

My friends rallied around to help me get settled. It wasn't easy. All the belongings that had fit so comfortably into modern, high-rise digs suddenly looked lost and lonely in my enormous, elegant, old-world new home. It looked so empty. I knew of course that it was a matter of time. It would take time and money to acquire all the furniture and rugs and lamps and things to fill the six enormous rooms. But still, I felt annoyed that I couldn't get things together the way I liked to get things together—instantly.

I was getting nervous. Suppose, God forbid, I had made a great big, expensive mistake? Well, it just couldn't be, that was all.

It didn't help when Alan told me that he hated the apartment. "It looks cold," he said.

It *was* cold, as a matter of fact. Who would've guessed that on the balmy spring day I first saw the place? Now that nippy weather was here, the place was chilly all the time. The bedroom, with its northern walls, was, in fact, icy when the heat went off at the stroke of midnight. I bought an electric heater and kept it running all the time, but the bedroom just never warmed up. And in spite of the fistfuls of vitamins I swallowed, I kept ending up in bed with sore throats.

I made an appointment to see my doctor. My nerves were really frayed and my sleep was no longer unbroken, even with the Placidyl. He tried to make me feel better by assuring me that more women flip out over decorating problems than over broken marriages. It was a well-known phenomenon. He felt sure that once I had my house in order I'd feel a lot more calm. In the meantime we'd try something a little different to get my nerves back in line. We'd try Eskalith at night, along with Valium. Since Eskalith was a lithium substance (and lithium had been used successfully to calm the mania of manic-depressives), it ought to relieve my anxiety. "But," my doctor chided, "I wish you hadn't taken on such a heavy load. It's an enormous responsibility, an apartment like that."

I decided to write another book. Perhaps Alan was right when he suggested that I really was suffering the "post-partum" depression that is common to writers, once the baby is finished, printed, and published; the old question, "What shall I do with the rest of my life?" What I needed was more challenge. I acquired a high-powered agent and submitted an outline for a book on sex. It would, the agent assured me, bring in an awful lot of money.

But I just couldn't shake the unnerving fear in the pit of my stomach. And I didn't understand it at all. Perhaps it was the apartment. It still didn't seem like home to me. The furniture from my old apartment sat like isolated little dollhouse pieces in the cavernous rooms, but I couldn't afford to buy anything just yet; I had to wait for the next royalty check to arrive.

While agents and lawyers conferred and told me I was rich and famous, I felt more and more frightened and invisible.

My father detected the hysterical tremor in my voice when he called one night. He'd never heard that before. Did I want him to fly up for a short visit? "Oh, Daddy," I broke down and sobbed, "please come."

With my father ensconced in the guest room, I felt safe somehow. "You just need some rugs on your floor," he assured me and I felt convinced he was right. The apartment problems were really minor. And so

I relaxed in the knowledge that my father was there, taking care of me, and we set out to enjoy New York. It was the first time I'd enjoyed New York in quite a while. We went to the theater, dined with friends, and toured the big-city sights.

Before he left, my father said he was worried that I seemed so nervous and even more worried that I seemed to rely so much on tranquilizers. Didn't I know that being "all pilled up" was the same as being drunk? I flinched at the phrase. It didn't seem consistent with any picture I had of myself. "All pilled up"? Sounded like a junkie. I tried to explain that I needed something to keep me calm through this momentary crisis, and God knows, I couldn't take a drink. A drink would kill me now that I'd had acute pancreatitis. And if I kept on being as nervous as I was now, then that would kill me too. I really didn't see that I had any options. I had to stay calm somehow, and besides, my doctor had prescribed the Valium. Surely he knew what was best for me. After all, hadn't he just saved my life? He surely wasn't going to endanger it now.

My father, who didn't seem convinced at all, went home to Alabama, leaving me alone, and scared, in the big, cold, empty apartment.

20.

Christmas was coming again. I'd never known a normal holiday—not in the crazy fashion business, where life was lived a season ahead of the calendar. Everybody was working like the devil in order to be able to have a few days free at Christmastime. I knew I had to get home to Alabama. That was the one known quantity in my life. And so I rushed around, photographing ball gowns in one studio, kiddies' sunsuits in another, and typing up stories in between photo sessions. Every night I came home late and, generally, I ate my dinner in the coffee shop on the corner. Somehow I never seemed to have the strength anymore to cook a meal. Sometimes I wondered why, but rationalized that the kitchen, with all its old, outmoded equipment, was just too inconvenient. And, anyway, I just didn't have the energy.

Everything was going so fast these days that I never seemed to be able to sort it out. The pages of my calendar seemed flipped by a gale wind; the days ran past as if daring me to catch up with them. I couldn't. All I could do was watch while life ran away with me.

Things were happening that worried me a lot—little, peculiar things I couldn't explain. I came home and found my apartment door wide open. I knew it hadn't been open when I left. I always locked my door.

And yet there it was. I rang for the elevator man, and together we walked through the apartment, but it was empty, and nothing seemed to have been disturbed. A week later a brand-new roll of stamps had vanished from a desk drawer where I'd put them the day before. Now I felt frightened. When I left for the holidays I carefully double-locked the apartment and gave the only key to my neighbor.

The week after Christmas, it seemed as if nobody had had a vacation at all. The office was a madhouse, with everybody trying to catch up from their few days off or working harder in anticipation of taking some time off at New Year's. We were all faced with pushed-forward deadlines and double loads of stories. The pace was frenetic. I wasn't surprised that I was developing a migraine.

It was a bad one—the first I'd had in a month or so. Oh, well, by now I knew what to do. I left the office early and went home to lie down. I'd take two Valium and two Fiorinal and try to sleep. But the headache throbbingly persisted. I took a Percodan. Finally, curled across the bed under a couple of blankets, I got to sleep.

The telephone woke me. Five times in all: Alan, Frannie, Erica, Greta, my mother. I explained to them all that I wasn't feeling well and I'd call them back. Finally I slept.

When I woke up, the headache had disappeared. After a couple of cups of coffee, there wasn't even the usual migraine hangover. Wonderful!

I returned the phone calls one by one. All five of them. But then something odd happened. My old friend Jim phoned and said, "What happened to you?"

"What do you mean, what happened to me?"

"I'm still waiting for you to call me back. You said . . ." and I listened incredulously as Jim gave a word-for-word recounting of the conversation he swore we'd had earlier. *But I didn't remember talking to Jim!* Was he sure? "Mary Ann, are you all right?" I really didn't know. I knew I was getting scared. Because I had no memory at all of talking with Jim.

I telephoned my doctor. "I'm really worried. I don't know what's going on. I keep forgetting things. No, it isn't forgetting—it's as if there were gaps in my consciousness, moments that just aren't there. Do you think I'm losing my mind? Could it be a brain tumor?"

My doctor was quiet for a moment. "I don't know. I don't think so. I think it's probably just the pressure. Pressure and tension can do strange things to people. But I do think we ought to have a neurologist look you over. Call me later. I'll arrange it for you."

We were going to have to do an electroencephalogram to check out the brain impulses, just to make sure everything was normal in there. I wasn't to worry—it was a mere medical formality. "I'm sure it's fine," my doctor tried to reassure me. I wasn't sure about anything anymore, and all the possibilities kept racing around the speedtrack of my mind. Brain tumor? Most likely. Insanity? Why not? Epilepsy? Oh God, the most likely of all. Please, no! Please let it turn out to be nothing at all! Please, God, let it turn out to be overwork! I swear I'll take it easy. Let it be overwork. I know how to deal with that.

I trudged alone to the neurologist's office after work, tired and nervous. I didn't know what to expect except that he would implant twenty-six needles in my head. "It won't hurt," he had told me. "It'll just mean a little bit of discomfort." It hurt.

We'd done the usual preliminary tests, of course. Stand on one foot, close your eyes, touch your nose. Everything checked out normal. Then a technician had swabbed off my scalp and implanted all the tiny electrodes. It wasn't unbearable, but it hurt, all right. The test began. For half an hour I followed all instructions—close your eyes, breathe deeply, pant—while the stylus wrote out messages about my brain that only the doctor could understand. Rapid breathing until I knew that I would soon lose consciousness, and then, thank heaven, "That's it—it's all over." They would let my doctor know the results.

My doctor read me the report. "The neurological examination was completely normal." He did not tell me that the report also read, "Shows certain hyperactivity which could be drug-related."

I should have been relieved, but I wasn't. There was still that nagging question in my mind. What *had* happened to those blocks of time?

By the first week in January I was in the hospital with a severe case of flu. My doctor had said, "I don't think you ought to be alone. I'd feel better hospitalizing you." While I was there he wanted to photograph my brain. Just to be absolutely certain all was well.

I lay still on a table, my head in a cap and held in a vise, while the technician shot dye into my veins, in preparation for the CAT scan. "The newest kind of X-rays," they'd told me. "Show up everything."

My doctor showed me the report. "Completely normal," it read.

In a week I was back at the *New York Times,* back on a split-second deadline schedule. Nothing, it seemed, ever got better at work.

21.

In the spring of 1975 (I couldn't quite believe the decade was half over) my agent sold the new book. After a week of harrowing negotiations, during which time I subsisted on Valium and coffee, I signed a contract that guaranteed me a six-figure advance. I had a year to write the book.

I was euphoric. Not only because this, at last, was going to be my ticket out of the *New York Times,* but because, starting right now, I could finally get my apartment together. And that was important, because I was sick and tired of camping out in somebody else's leftover mess. I wanted my apartment to look like me, so I could begin to feel at home.

I found a decorator. As soon as I saw the approving smile playing across his face, I knew that he, like I, had fallen in love with the big yellow room. "I like the color," he said. "We'll leave it." I excitedly handed over my apartment problems to the professional who was going to solve them all. And hang the cost! Well, within limits.

The work was to start in April—it would be a birthday present to myself. Both the decorator and his contractor felt they could work a lot faster in an uninhabited apartment, so I packed my duds and took off for Europe. It was the first real vacation I'd had in a decade.

I went to Paris and London where I visited with friends and was wined and dined everywhere as a visiting member of the press. But something was missing. For one thing, I was terribly lonely. Why was it I never had anyone to travel with? Why was it I couldn't have Alan? I didn't seem to be enjoying anything so much anymore. Not the way I used to. And I felt very, very tired. All the time.

I returned to an apartment full of plaster dust and workmen. There would be another month of chaos and confusion before the huge apartment would be completed. Meanwhile, I'd just have to get used to the mess and work around it.

I plunged back into my work at the paper. There was no question of working on the new book until the apartment was ready and I had a proper office.

The newest regime at the *Times* seemed to be shaky, and we felt the pressure. Our department got flak from the higher-ups every day of the week. We had meetings about stories, meetings about photographers, meetings about layouts, and finally meetings about meetings. When the meetings were over none of us seemed to know any better just what was expected of us. The mood seemed to change from meeting to meeting; what was acceptable last week was not acceptable now. We wondered just how it was that we were supposed to produce stories at all, much less good stories. Stories that were fit to print.

There was simply never enough time, and the days sped by. I was in a squirrel cage that spun faster and faster. I had to keep reminding myself that, once the new book was out, I would finally be free. If I could only hang on that long! Until then I'd just have to keep my jittery nerves under control. The best way to do that was with Valium. Meanwhile, I'd show my feelings to no one and, at the paper, I'd continue to sit with my back to the wall.

The apartment was finished at last. I was ecstatic. It looked exactly the way I'd dreamed it would: a country house right in the middle of Manhattan. The geraniums bloomed in the window boxes again, bright red enclosed by the white shutters. The room's soft yellow walls still changed with the passing clouds, but the rest of the room was all crisp blue and white, in a mélange of checks and patterns. Delft plates stood in the old red-painted Pennsylvania china cupboard, next to the seventeenth-century gateleg table that was my pride and joy. Bookshelves lined two walls and held not only the library but all the treasures I'd collected all those years. Feathery green ferns in baskets lined the fireplace, where, come winter, I'd have a roaring, blazing fire. The study had been painted red—tomato-soup red I'd told them, tomato-soup red I'd gotten—a soft, creamy, lilting color. There was a table that would be the envy of any writer—six feet square and solid as Gibraltar. The study was made for working and it made me eager to begin.

But it was the bedroom that had been most transformed. The walls had been padded to keep out the winter wind, and covered in tiny blue-and-white checks. A blue-and-white schoolhouse quilt hung on the wall, while other quilts changed the look of the bed each day, according to my mood. Most of my friends had the same comment: "Wow!" Alan, on the other hand, looked at the bedroom and said, "It still looks cold to me."

By summer I was closeted in the apartment, working on the new book. I didn't have to worry about turning down weekend invitations—there weren't any. All my friends had gone off in different directions. Frannie had moved to California, Greta and Nils had gone to Vermont, even Alan had taken his family off to Connecticut—a move that, while it had absolutely no effect on our time together, made him seem even more unavailable than before. Alan never mentioned leaving his wife anymore, though he still complained about how unhappy he was. I simply ignored it, most of the time.

And so I stayed in the city on weekends and worked, while the powerful air conditioners hummed away (I thanked God the electricity was included in the maintenance charge), keeping the huge apartment frosty-cool. I felt as if I were the only person left in New York.

I wasn't sleeping well. Although I continued to take Placidyl, Eskalith, and Valium each night, I still got no more than six or seven hours of fretful sleep. I decided I ought to go back to my shrink. He said he would see me right after his August vacation.

My own August vacation from the *Times* was spent in my apartment, working on the book.

By autumn I still wasn't sleeping well, in spite of therapy. Every morning I awoke at five-thirty with my heart racing in what felt like unremitting fear. But what was I afraid of? There was nothing any different in my life. The same work, the same pressures, the same people. But, regular as an alarm clock, my pounding heart jolted me out of my fitful sleep, each and every morning before dawn.

My shrink thought he had an answer. He would give me a smaller dose of Placidyl, 200 milligrams, to take in the morning. That would keep me asleep until the more respectable hour of 8:00 A.M. The new Placidyl were little, round and red perles. I put them next to the big green capsules and the medium-sized red ones in my medicine cabinet.

The *Times* was abuzz with gossip: several of the bigwigs were going to get canned unless they could get their departments in line. In these austere days at the paper, this meant cutting budgets. The bosses all seemed nervous and jumpy, and their concern showed up in their crankiness with the underlings. Tempers were short, and there were raised voices and lots of martini breath after lunch. Erica and I lunched together every day and commiserated with one another. Her department, it seemed, was as chaotic as ours. "The only good thing about my job," she laughed, "is lunch." Our lunch hours were getting longer as we tried to spend less and less time in an office where the tension was tangible.

I was under enormous pressure to finish the second section of my book. As the advance had been so large, one stipulation had been that it would be finished, and presented, in three parts—just to make it a bit easier on the publisher's pocketbook. But my own pocketbook was in trouble. "How do you manage to spend so much money?" my lawyer asked me. The bills for the work on the apartment had come in. They added up to around fifty thousand dollars. The only thing for me to do was to work even faster. When I trudged in from the *Times* every day I went right to the typewriter in my cheerful red study, not coming out until late at night, when I wearily went to bed for another night of not-so-sound sleep.

There were problems with the book. The editor and I didn't see eye to eye on what it should be. She was adamant about what she did and didn't want; I was equally adamant about what I would and would not do. My agent was acting as go-between, and he too was ready to throw in the towel. But I couldn't do that. I needed the money.

Late in October I developed a sore throat and fever that didn't go away. For five days all I could do was sleep.

When I finally was able to get out of bed, the scale showed 116 pounds. *I had gained twelve pounds!* But that simply wasn't possible. I checked again. One sixteen on the nose.

I was frightened. How could anybody gain twelve pounds lying in bed and not eating for five days?

The next morning the scale read 102. Now I was really scared.

For the next few days my weight swung daily between 120 and 102, with occasional stops in between. Some days I couldn't zip my jeans, other days they drooped insanely. I was beginning to feel insane myself. But there was no mistaking the numbers on the scale. Something was very, very wrong.

There were other strange things happening as well. Whenever I closed my eyes I saw strange, dark shapes. Shapes like bats, gargoyles, flitting around behind my closed eyelids like some gruesome hallucination. I asked my shrink what he thought it could mean. Was I going crazy? I seemed to feel just a little bit crazy a lot of the time these days. My shrink immediately asked, "How many Valium are you taking per day?" "Never more than eight," I told him, "two five-milligrams, four times a day." "Mary Ann, you're having a typical addiction reaction. I want you to cut down on your Valium."

Me? Addicted to Valium? I was terrified to take any more Valium at all, in spite of the fact that my nerves seemed to be running away with me. No, I just wouldn't take any more Valium—not right now. Alan came and wrapped me in blankets and watched me shake. He looked worried, but I was too sick to reassure him and so we sat together for the whole day and I didn't even ask how he would explain it to his wife. And, when I had to sign a check, Alan held my hand down to steady it. It was the only way I could write my name.

Two days passed before the chills and the shaking stopped and the dark shapes began to disappear. I swore that I would never again be stupid enough to exceed six Valium a day. My limit would be six 5-milligram tablets. That amount, the doctor assured me, was safe.

I went back to work, feeling exhausted. I couldn't remember when I'd last felt well. It seemed to me my body was simply giving out. I had just passed forty, and I wondered if this was what it felt like to get old.

My doctor thought perhaps I ought to go home to Alabama again— just for a week or two, to see whether it would have the same magical recuperative powers as before. I asked for, and got, a week's vacation from the *Times*. I was sure I'd get well in Alabama. I always had before.

"You look fine," my parents told me at the airport.

"Well, I sure don't feel it," I replied, pointing out the swollen glands in my throat. "I feel like hell."

My childhood doctor had died the previous year, but my father's doctor came to see me. He was a cheerful man, the sort that always makes a patient feel in good hands, but I thought he tended toward overmedication.

"It's probably just a virus," he smilingly told me. "I want you to eat lots of ice cream and get these prescriptions filled."

"But Doctor, I can't eat lots of ice cream; I've got terrible hypoglycemia."

"Now, Mary Ann, you want to get well, don't you?"

My father had the prescriptions filled. I never found out what they were for. I really didn't care anymore. I just took the pills.

After one day of ice cream and pills, I felt far worse. I had a fever of 101 degrees and felt terribly weak. I suspected my blood sugar was the problem and I gave up the ice cream. But my throat still hurt terribly and I felt feverish, sweaty, weak, shaky, and very depressed.

"Well, you won't do what the doctor told you, Mary Ann," my father said. "I just don't understand you. You always think you know more than anybody else. You never *have* been willing to do what you're told. I'm *not* going to tell the doctor you won't do what he tells you to."

I heard myself screaming in anger: "You don't *care* what happens to me, you've *never* cared what happened to me. Leave me alone, God damn it! Can't you see I'm sick? I don't care if I die. Just leave me alone. I don't need you. I don't want to see you anymore!" My father angrily strode out of the room, slamming the door behind him. I sobbed, "I can't take it anymore, I can't. I want to die. I don't care. . . ." I saw my mother's frightened face and heard her say, "Oh God, Mary Ann, please!"

I told my mother I had to get out of there, had to get back to New York, where my own doctor, I prayed, could help me. Somebody just had to help me.

My mother took me to the plane the next day. I flew back to New York and went directly to my doctor's office.

"I feel like kissing the floor," I told the nurses. "I've never been so glad to be anywhere in my life as I am to be in this office right now."

"Does this hurt?" my doctor asked, touching my throat. I leaped up from the table as the tears started.

"I think you have thyroiditis," he told me. "Your thyroid is protruding from your neck."

Two days later the lab tests confirmed it: viral thyroiditis. Relatively rare, my doctor told me, but not serious. There was nothing to do but let it run its course. That could take anywhere from a few weeks to a year. Seeing the panic in my eyes, my doctor tried to reassure me. "I have to tell you the possibilities, but I don't think for a moment it is going to take that long. We'll just have to wait and see." We would forgo the only known remedy for the disease—cortisone—because he didn't want to subject me to its serious side effects. Instead, I should take two aspirin every four hours until the infection went away. And wait.

There was absolutely no question of my going to work again. It was going to mean another medical leave—three months at least.

22.

I cried a lot, and when I wasn't crying I was sleeping. I was still having violent mood swings and violent weight swings as well. I felt frantic about being so out of control of virtually everything.

My shrink decided to try one of the antidepressant drugs as a means of bringing my now erratic emotions into a more temperate line. Navane was the drug of choice.

Its effect was swift and miraculous. Within a matter of days, as if by magic, my mind seemed to click back into place, and for the first time in months I felt like myself again—not physically, but I could think clearly and everything was back in its proper emotional perspective. I wondered what it was I had fought with my father about. I called him in Alabama to tell him how sorry I was, that it hadn't been me at all; it had been the damned thyroiditis.

I was to take Navane three times a day—when I woke up, at noon, and at five o'clock. My life was controlled by the clock, because I knew better than to miss a single dose of Navane, though I could always tell by the stirring of little butterfly wings in my stomach when dose time had arrived.

My doctors assured me it was simply a question of keeping head and psyche together until the malfunctioning thyroid stopped tormenting me. When it was healed I would function normally all by myself. They promised I would.

I kept myself together with a variety of medicines: Navane for my emotional state; aspirin and tetracycline for the infected thyroid gland; Kanulase for my delicate pancreas; Papase (a papaya enzyme) for bloat; Eskalith and Placidyl for the eight hours' sleep I needed, plus Valium to keep my nerves under control; Fiorinal for migraines; Librax for when a pancreas attack seemed imminent; Percodan if it really occurred; antihistamines, sinus decongestants, and nasal sprays; vitamins and minerals. It was becoming harder and harder to find room for all the bottles in the medicine cabinet, let alone in my pillbox.

In January I had an accident. I got out of bed and pitched over backward, with no warning at all. The doctor who X-rayed me said I was lucky I hadn't broken something. How on earth had it happened? I didn't know. But it was to be just the first in a series of peculiar and inexplicable accidents.

I was having more trouble sleeping. My shrink switched me to Dalmane. It made me feel dreadful, but I stuck with it.

One night I couldn't get to sleep. I tossed and turned, feeling the panic rise. The Dalmane wasn't working. Perhaps I should take another. Surely two wouldn't hurt. I don't remember if I took a third, but I fell to the floor, and it took all my strength to pull myself back into bed. Eventually I slept.

Morning came. When I tried to get out of bed, I fell once more. I was terrified. I weakly dialed my doctor's telephone number, but the answering service said he was unavailable. His covering doctor would return my call. A stranger phoned. "Make sure you don't put anything stronger than an aspirin into your body for the next twenty-four hours," he told me. "You'll be all right."

But I wasn't sure I would be. I telephoned Erica and asked her to come over. "I almost killed myself," I told her. I didn't really know whether or not I had tried to kill myself, but the thought scared me, and I just didn't want to be alone. Not in that big, empty apartment where the quiet was resoundingly loud by now. I needed company. Maybe that's what was wrong with me anyway.

Erica stayed with me for the remainder of the weekend. On Monday

I telephoned my shrink to say that I didn't want to take Dalmane again.

The fact is that suicide was never very far from my mind. It wasn't that I was planning it; I just didn't want to go on living if it meant living the way I was now. I felt so exhausted from being ill all the time, and I couldn't even remember, by now, how I'd felt before I got sick. I seemed to bounce from one illness to the next, with no breathing space in between. I felt like the ball in some wild pinball machine, flipped about on little swingarms by an unseen, sadistic player. I didn't know whether it was God who was playing those games with me or not, but I did know that if this was life, then I didn't really want it. This sort of game I didn't have the strength to play anymore. I'd rather be dead. I thought about that more and more: giving up would be the easiest thing to do.

I told my mother one day how I felt, but she cried and begged me not to talk like that. My friends, on the other hand, seemed to believe me. As I told them, I'd be better off dead than half dead, wouldn't I?

I had another accident. I lost my balance and almost fell out a window. I knew what the papers would have said: "Fell or jumped to her death." Nobody, knowing my feelings about suicide, would have believed "fell."

On a Sunday morning (why did these things always happen on weekends?) toward the end of January, I discovered I couldn't talk coherently. When I telephoned a friend, he said, "What's wrong with you? You sound like you've had a few." He knew I didn't drink anymore and said he'd come over in an hour if I wasn't feeling better. But within an hour the symptoms had disappeared.

When I swallowed my next dose of Navane, it happened again. Now it sank in: I was having side effects from the Navane. There was nothing to do but live with them until I could reach my shrink the next day. I was afraid to skip the Navane—that might be worse yet. So I sat in my big apartment, alone, unable to make any words come out of my mouth, until Monday.

My shrink decided he'd try an antidote for the side effects, to be taken along with the Navane. My speech difficulties, he explained, were one of the common adverse effects of long-term therapy with antidepressants. He prescribed Cogentin to counteract them. Thus began a therapy of drugs to cure drugs. It was a therapy that would change the course of my life completely.

But nothing was cured by the Cogentin. By the next day, I still couldn't control my speech. I was embarrassed to talk to anyone except close friends. Everybody else would surely think me drunk.

My shrink said Navane would have to go. We would try another of the myriad antidepressant drugs on the market. We began two weeks of trial-and-error medication, while I once again shook and shivered from the thyroid infection, which had not abated at all.

Systematically, we worked our way through Elavil, Mellaril, Tofranil, and Triavil, plus several others I can't remember. One made me nauseated; the next affected my vision. One dried out my mouth; the next made my heart flutter. My shrink kept urging me to give each a fair trial, but I just couldn't ask my poor body to go through much more. The drugs weren't helping my depression at all—they were depressing me. Each made me feel worse than the last, while I continued to manifest the pseudo-psychotic symptoms of the thyroid disease. My behavior ranged from somnambulant to manic, and I never knew what the next day would bring. My weight continued to fluctuate wildly.

After a few weeks of experimentation with the new drugs, I angrily went through the medicine cabinet and pitched twenty or so pill bottles into the garbage. I just wasn't going to try any of those anymore. I really wanted (and needed) the Navane.

And so, with my shrink's permission, I tried it again. Within a matter of hours, I was once again mumbling incoherently. My shrink ordered me to stop the Navane.

We were all getting kind of desperate—my shrink, my doctor, and I. I wasn't able to control my moods or my behavior. My shrink and my doctor conferred and decided I should try Ritalin. Although Ritalin was a stimulant, it had been used successfully in the treatment of hyperkinetic children. Perhaps it would calm me.

With the first dose of Ritalin, I miraculously drifted once more into seminormality. The irrational behavior calmed into a semblance of sanity, and I felt better than I had in weeks. I began to think that maybe I could make it after all. Maybe I'd be able to hang on just long enough for the thyroid to cure itself. I hoped that wouldn't take much longer.

I was getting calls from the office. Just how long did I plan to be out? Was I really ill? What was the matter with me? They wanted me to come in and be checked out by the *Times*'s doctor. Erica telephoned: "They think you're goofing off."

I got dressed for my first long outing in months—the thirty-block trip to the *New York Times*. The *Times* doctor examined my still-swollen throat. "Thyroiditis," he said, and sent me home. The company continued, however reluctantly, to forward my checks. But time was running out. My leave of absence would be up in three more weeks. What would I do then?

Somehow I had managed to turn in the second section of my book. By writing a few pages each day, I had done what I considered a commendable job. But my editor didn't think so; she wanted rewrites, and I wasn't prepared to do them. I liked the book the way it was, and I raised holy hell. It had never been my style to fight with editors—on the contrary, I'd always gotten along with them. I was, they had told me, "easy to edit."

But now I was crying a lot and screaming to my agent that I just wouldn't do it. Eventually my agent persuaded me to give them what they wanted—we'd take the money and run—so I wearily agreed to do the rewriting. But not now; I wasn't going to do any writing for a while. I couldn't. Besides, the final deadline wasn't until June.

Through these three months of being confined to my apartment my life was limited to trying to keep my head (and my emotions) on an even keel. Aside from that, I didn't do much of anything. I spoke with Alan every day, and he came to see me regularly. We rarely made love anymore. I simply didn't have the energy, and he didn't seem to have the inclination. I rationalized that I couldn't be very attractive to any man. After all, men don't have much patience with illness. And I was ill, it seemed, all the time now.

It was becoming more and more difficult to sleep. I was afraid to try Dalmane again, so I was now stuck with Placidyl (I'd given up Eskalith as worthless) and a certain amount of Valium. I didn't want to violate the six-per-day Valium limit, because I didn't want to risk addiction again. As a result, some nights I had no sleep at all. And when I couldn't sleep I felt simply terrified. For one thing, I felt afraid of my apartment. I couldn't quite put my finger on what it was that frightened me, but I knew I felt afraid to be alone.

Erica came to spend the night, but she slept only fitfully as I wandered the rooms all night long. Sarah took over the next night. She and I talked most of the night, and she too went home exhausted.

When I ran out of friends to spend the night, I hired a nurse. For the next two weeks, at thirty dollars a night, she sat in the living room with the lights on while I lay in the bedroom with the lights on. Then I could no longer afford her. I would simply have to shiver alone. Which is exactly what I did.

At the end of the month, I got my druggist's bill: six hundred seventy-five dollars. No, it was not a mistake. (I checked it carefully.)

My leave of absence was over; I had to return to work if I wanted to keep my job. My doctor was concerned about that. He would allow me to go back to the office only if I could work half days. Surely a company like the *Times* could accommodate recuperation. He wanted me to leave work at three each day and go home to bed.

The *Times*'s doctor agreed. They'd keep a watchful eye on me.

The night before I was to return to work, I fell in the shower. I don't know how long I was out, or if I was out at all. After a few minutes (I guess) I was able to pull myself out and get shakily into bed. But it seemed very odd to me. I didn't know how it had happened.

My boss's first words the next morning were "I want you out in the market and I don't want you to return to the office before six. That is the schedule we work here."

I tried. I dragged myself on my rounds and sat for as long as I could at each appointment. My legs would barely hold me upright. They felt as if they had heavy weights chained to them. My friends on Seventh Avenue were concerned. They had never seen me look so tired. I didn't explain my illness to them. I just said I'd been sick for a while.

There was a heavy snow in March. I stoically kept all of my appointments for the day. By the time I returned to the office, my throat had begun to hurt. By the next day, the fever had returned. I was ordered back into bed. The doctors all feared the thyroid infection would flare up again. It did.

I was right back where I had started—sick and scared. There was nothing I could do except lie in bed and shiver. No amount of Ritalin, Valium, or Placidyl helped me sleep, not when my thyroid was running on "high." During those periods, I cried nonstop, lost weight overnight, and looked like a ghost. When my thyroid was underactive, I was lethargic, slept around the clock, and gained enormous amounts of weight from one day to the next. Nobody could tell me if or when I could hope to feel better.

My doctor decided we'd better try thyroid medication and continue to use tetracycline to help keep the infection under control.

On March 15, 1976, he entered on my chart: "Fuzzy-headed. Blurred vision. Cries a lot. Valium, Synthroid, Dexamyl." He had added amphetamine, he told me later, to try to keep me on my feet.

My boss telephoned, waking me from one of my lethargy sleeps, screaming, "Who is going to do all this work? How do you think it makes me look? I want you to do it, and I want you to do it *now!*"

I put the receiver down. It was all over. I could never return to the paper. I would have to resign.

The forms were processed. The union was on my side. The paper owed me something for all those years, they said. We negotiated a separation settlement, and I stayed away from the office, refusing to talk to my boss. I wasn't about to die for the *New York Times*. Somehow I would manage.

On March 21, 1976, my ten-year tenure with the paper was terminated. I was free at last. I was also alone.

23.

I had nothing to fall back on except the unfinished book. I only hoped that the tiny settlement I'd extracted from the *Times* would tide me over until the money from the book came in. My expenses were terribly high, what with bills for the apartment, assorted bills from lawyers, accountants, and business managers, plus the ever-rising medical bills. There didn't seem to be much I could do about those. Or about my drugstore bill, which hovererd around four hundred dollars a month. I really had to try to get the book out as quickly as possible.

But Ritalin was no longer doing the job of keeping me calm, and my mood swings, from lethargy to mania, were more violent than ever. I just couldn't stand the way I felt, and one Saturday morning, without my shrink's permission, I took the matter into my own hands. I swallowed a Navane. It was like a miracle! I felt better immediately, and, thanks be to God, I could still talk. The two-month respite had done the job, and Navane was going to work for me again. I was both elated and terribly relieved. Perhaps I could function like a normal person once more.

My doctor kept an ever-close watch on my thyroid, taking blood samples at regular intervals. They still showed active thyroiditis, but at least now, with the Navane, I was functional.

I was maintained on doses of Navane, Valium, Synthroid (synthetic thyroid hormone), Dexamyl (for the lethargy), tetracycline, Placidyl, and Kanulase, along with vitamins and minerals, Percodan, Fiorinal, antihistamines, and sinus decongestants, taken as needed. My silver pill-box had long ago become inadequate. I now carried the vials in my handbag.

Now that I no longer had the paper to contend with, I could concentrate full-time on writing. The book was slowly but surely coming along, and at the end of the road was a great pot of gold. The thought kept me typing full speed. But full speed wasn't fast enough. I was finding, to my chagrin, that it was becoming difficult for me to type. My fingers seemed inordinately stiff all of a sudden. For a while I chalked it up to exhaustion and the fact that I had never been an accurate typist in the first place. But somehow the inaccuracies were multiplying.

My handwriting had changed noticeably, too, and my fingers felt cramped and tired whenever I so much as signed my name. My shrink said he thought it might be the Navane. I knew that giving up Navane was out of the question, so I resigned myself to typing pitifully incorrect copy, very slowly indeed. The pot of gold would have to wait a while longer.

For the next month or so, I made sure I got all of my medicines at the proper hours to keep me functional throughout the day. I wrote for as many hours as I could. The rest of the time I wandered the rooms, talked on the phone, and, whenever I could, saw Alan. He was terribly supportive about the book and kept saying, "You've got to start thinking about your *next* book. You should get started on an outline now." But I kept telling him I really didn't have the strength to think about another project just yet. Let me finish this one first. Then I'd think about what I was going to do with the rest of my life.

I was relieved to have Alan to talk things over with. I relied heavily on his advice, his opinions, his counsel about the book. In fact, I relied heavily on Alan for just about everything and thanked God every day that I had someone like him to look after me. We saw each other daily and, once in a while, we made love. As far as I was concerned, it had developed into a comfortable relationship. Alan had become my best friend. We never discussed "being in love" anymore, and he no longer mentioned leaving his wife.

I had problems with unusual menstrual bleeding. Occasionally I would skip a month, and since I had no reason to fear pregnancy now that my love life was almost nonexistent, I worried about dread possibilities—like cancer. My gynecologist was sure that it was menopause, but, at forty, I wasn't ready to believe that.

There was a polyp on my uterus that would have to come off. In the gynecologist's office, without anesthesia, I lay quietly and stoically while the doctor probed and cut inside my uterus. At one point he looked up and said, "Are you still there?" I nodded. By now I had gotten used to being in pain. It seemed to be my lot in life.

Back at home, though, I took a couple of Percodan to make up for the pain I'd already endured. Something only an addict would do. But I didn't know that then.

24.

The book was finally finished. I thought that at last I'd be able to rest a bit, but the editor wanted more changes. I was furious. I couldn't control my anger, and the editor and I had interminable, frustrating telephone conversations. Finally, my agent prevailed upon me to make the requested changes. And to try, in the future, to keep my temper under control. It was weeks before there was peace again.

As a matter of fact, I was a little surprised at the way I was blowing up at people these days, but I attributed it to that old bogey, my "redhead temperament." It never crossed my mind that my personality change was drug related.

My doctor said to me one day, "I wish you would sell that apartment. You haven't been well a minute since you've lived there." He was right. Maybe it was the apartment itself—the responsibility, the financial drain—that was making me sick. Perhaps it was too big for me to handle. Well, I'd just sell it and go back to renting. At least then the responsibility would all be the landlord's and I could go back to my carefree ways.

I put my big, beautiful apartment on the market, and within two weeks it was sold. I had to move—fast.

I found a smaller, more modern (and therefore, I hoped, more easily maintained) apartment in a brand-new tall glass tower. A desirable building, though more oil-rich than old-rich. I would take possession in June—a month away.

Easter came, that year, on my birthday. Friends rallied around to help me celebrate, and we all went off to the Easter parade and lunch at the Plaza. Maybe it was the spring air, but I felt better than I had for months. I looked haggard and terribly thin, but I reasoned that no one on earth could possibly look healthy after an ordeal such as the one I'd endured. At least my nerves were more or less under control, as long as I remembered to take the Navane three times a day. And what Navane didn't do, Valium did, although it occasionally took three Valium to do the job. But I wasn't seeing any more dark shapes and I saw no signs of any more addiction. I supposed I had finally accustomed my body to the Valium it needed. Anyway, I wasn't going to question anything. Not as long as I was beginning to feel more like a normal human being. Most of the time, in fact, I felt pretty much in control. Pretty calm. It didn't matter that it was artificial calm.

By mid-June I was more or less ensconced in an elegant thirty-sixth-floor aerie with a spectacular view of upper Central Park to the west, the Hudson River to the north, and lower Fifth Avenue and the Empire State Building to the south. There was no denying that the view was beautiful. But one thing worried me. The building—and especially my apartment—seemed so removed from everything. I had no idea I would be the only tenant on the floor most of the time. The oil-rich Arabians, it appeared, were transient tenants at best. The stillness in my apartment was almost audible, and my only companions were the birds that once in a while flew that high. Oh, well, the quiet ought to be good for my writing. Except that I didn't have anything to write.

My days settled into a pattern. I had nothing to do except wait for the galley proofs of the book to arrive. I couldn't seem to get myself together enough to do another book outline, even though Alan kept urging me to get on with it. The most I could do was get dressed in the morning and go down to Alan's office to have lunch with him, then back to my apartment for an afternoon nap. I didn't know how I'd ever made it before without a nap. I could sleep then with no insomnia at all, and I reasoned it was probably because I wasn't worrying about sleep that it came so easily by day. I treasured my nap, and I usually headed for bed about two in the afternoon, took a couple of Valium to make sure the pounding heart slowed down, and then slept until five. Then I got up, went to a coffee shop for a sandwich, and jittered around until time for bed (and Placidyl).

I couldn't make up my mind whether to go back to work. The thought of a nine-to-five job didn't seem so enchanting, especially since I wasn't sure I had the strength yet to work long hours. The days sped by, and nothing happened in my life.

Alan and I spoke on the telephone every morning. One day late in July, I picked up the phone to hear him say:

"I left home this morning."

"What do you mean? Of course you did. You do that every morning. What are you talking about?"

"I mean I finally left home."

My heart stopped beating. Alan had left his wife. The pounding started again. "How? What happened? What will you do?" My emotions spun out of control and within split seconds I felt relief, anxiety, curiosity, panic, love, longing, and fear. Alan was free. I could see him all the time now. But I heard an inner voice, "Is that what you both really want?"

Alan took an apartment only a few blocks from mine. Somehow the question of our living together never came up. From the moment he moved my life-style changed. Now I contended with having a man around the house, often for twenty-four hours at a stretch. Alan, understandably, felt displaced and strange being a bachelor again. And, while I wanted to see him happy and comfortable, I missed my time alone. I felt crowded and cranky, and it was difficult to remember I once dreamed of a lifetime of wedded bliss with Alan. Or with anyone else, for that matter. Perhaps my girlhood intuitions had been right all along. Maybe I just wasn't cut out for marriage.

By August I was bored. There was nothing to do around the house, and the quiet was beginning to get on my nerves. I found myself thinking nostalgically of the apartment of my carefree days—the one on Seventy-fourth Street, where all the times seemed like good times. But everybody else thought my new apartment was beautiful. "Perfect," they said. "How did you do it?" So I decided it must just be me. Something must be wrong with me.

My health seemed to have improved. The infected thyroid was slowly going back down to normal, thanks to the thyroid medication and antibiotics, which I continued to take.

I still didn't feel like looking for a job, so I went to Alan's office a lot, where I worked for free, just to be doing something.

Money was getting to be important. The move and the new apartment had eaten up most of the six-figure advance, and the new book wouldn't be out until the following spring. I was going to have to find a new source of income.

I wrote the outline for a new diet book. In October I submitted it to my agent and told him I was going home to Alabama for a rest. I'd wait for his call there. Once more, I packed my things and headed for home.

I hung around Alabama for a month, but there was nothing to do there, either. My father was always at the office, my friends were occupied with husbands and children, or jobs, and my mother, recovering from a bout of flu, wasn't well enough to go about much with me. The soothing of the soul I'd always found before whenever I came "home" to the South just wasn't there anymore.

The call from my agent never came. I decided he was either doing something wrong or doing nothing, so on Halloween I flew back to New York, where I found the door to my apartment smeared with paint. Trick or treat! Welcome home.

There was no market for that particular book my agent told me. Perhaps if I tried another subject. And so I wrote yet another outline, and submitted it to my agent with a note urging him to get on with things. Time was flying, and I needed the money.

On November 11, 1976, my doctor entered the following on my chart:

Can't keep eyes open.
Gaining weight.
Swollen feet.

The weight gain had stuck, and I now weighed 112 pounds. My stomach was bloated and distended. Nothing seemed to help. I frantically swallowed Librax in the hopes that the poked-out stomach was the result of nervous spasms. The swollen feet I couldn't explain either, and

I was going broke buying shoes in different sizes in the hopes of finding something comfortable. My closet was filled with shoes that fit when I bought them but later squeezed my toes. One of my friends complained, "Mary Ann, you can't just keep on buying shoes. You've got to find out what's going on!" I was trying to find out, but nobody seemed to know.

I could barely keep my eyes open during the day. I felt lethargic and drowsy all the time. My limbs felt heavy as lead, and often I took a cab for three or four blocks, when I felt I just wasn't going to make it.

I was taking the Navane three times a day, to keep my head together, and it was still affecting my handwriting but I realized I didn't have much choice about that. The Navane was keeping me out of the psycho ward, I felt sure.

By December my chart read:

Staggering, chilly, no energy.
On Euthroid, Dyazide.

In a sort of last-ditch attempt to control my inexplicable weight gain and bloat, my doctor had resorted to diuretics. He also wanted to try a different thyroid medication. Both of us hoped that if we took care of the thyroid, we would also be taking care of whatever was making me so chilly all the time. Most of the time I shivered with the cold, no matter how hot I kept my apartment.

25.

The new year of 1977 entered my life while I was asleep. I was to spend most of that year sleeping.

Nothing ever seemed to happen in my life anymore. It didn't seem like much of a life at all. I felt as if I were hurtling down a chute into nothingness, flinging off great space-junk pieces of reality as I fell. And if I seemed perfectly all right to everyone else, within the confines of my skin I felt quite unreal. As if my body had died long ago and my soul remained, roaming the earth without purpose.

Events in my life, however, continued to take place, regardless of my growing inability to perceive them.

I saw Alan every day and we had dinner together almost every night. We now made love again, often, and it was as beautiful as it had been in the beginning. I was grateful that I now had Alan to take care of me full-time. I felt so awfully tired that I really didn't have the strength to take care of myself anymore. But Alan was so strong, so all-knowing, and so caring—so *there*. I relied on him, most of all, to tell me that everything was going to be all right, eventually, and that, if I would only be patient, I would soon sell another book and my life would be back in place once again. When he said those things, my downward slide in the chute was halted. If only for a moment.

In the spring I was rushed to a hospital emergency room to have a catheter inserted in my nonfunctioning bladder. Nobody seemed to know just why it had stopped functioning, though the urologist suggested it could have been the codeine I'd taken for an especially intense migraine. A week later I was more or less OK again, though I resolved to treat codeine with more respect.

I had plastic surgery to correct my drooping eyelids (the result, the doctor told me, of too many sunburns that summer of 1970). I vomited for twelve hours after the operation. No one knew why. Though the operation was a success and removed the surplus skin, the lids still drooped over my pupils, making me look half-asleep all the time. I assumed that was what happened in middle age—I had passed forty, after all. No one, of course, ever considered the drugs.

I made a cursory effort to find a job, but my heart wasn't in it. My days had become devotions to sleep; the most important and most eagerly anticipated event of the day was my nap. At night I slept only fitfully between my different doses of Placidyl. The big 750-milligram capsule at bedtime, the medium-size 500 in the wee hours, and the tiny 200 at dawn. It was like a comical, medical Goldilocks: "How long did you sleep on my size?" asked the Papa Pill in his deep green voice. "And how long on my size?" asked the Medium Red Mama.

Since I was too tired to work full-time, I took on a couple of freelance assignments, which I worked on fitfully and with no real effort. Effort just wasn't possible. Both assignments were returned to me as unacceptable. I was stunned and furious. How did these people have the nerve to suggest my work wasn't good? They must be idiots. Never mind—I'd do it over and show them. And so I did. But secretly I wondered whether I'd lost my best-selling touch.

I also wondered why I kept losing my temper so easily, and resolved to be more careful about that in the future. I'd just have to explain to the editors that I was under a terrible strain right now.

In the summer I took a few short trips and had a few minor automobile accidents. I sideswiped a fender while trying to park (Damn! I've gotten out of practice with parallel parking), backed into a parked car

("I'm so sorry! I can't understand why I didn't see you!"), opened a car door and smashed my eye (six stitches). A friend who was with me the first time said, "Mary Ann, I think you're taking too many pills," but I said, "You're nuts—didn't you see what a tight squeeze it was?" I wondered what on earth he was talking about. I hadn't taken anything that day except the usual doses of the things my doctor had ordered me to take.

Still, it was a nuisance carrying a suitcase just for my pills, but I had to be sure I had them all with me: the Navane, and the Cogentin, and all the thyroid medicine; the Papase, Kanulase, Librax, Fiorinal, Valium, phenobarbital, Percodan, and codeine; plus my nasal sprays, anti-gas tablets, and stool softeners, and, certainly, the glycerine suppositories, plus Ducolax (in case the suppositories didn't work) and Lomotil (in case they worked too well). In addition, I carried thirty or so bottles of vitamins and minerals. God knows, I needed those!

I badgered my agent about the book sale. Had he really been doing anything about it or was he just sitting on the outlines? When he could produce only two people he'd shown it to, I fired him and began to search for a new, more competent agent.

It was a super-hot summer and Son of Sam was stalking the streets of New York making everybody edgy. I decided to drive out to Southampton to visit a friend and to get a bit of sea air. I didn't relish the long drive alone, but Alan hadn't been invited, and I just couldn't bring myself to get on the train—it was too confining. At least with a car I could always leave whenever I wanted to. Lately I couldn't stand being closed in anywhere. Not even in the subway. It felt really scary. Well, I always had been a bit claustrophobic. But I could stand the Hamptons for only one night. I drove back to the city the very next morning.

"Why do you suppose I can't seem to get out of the house alone anymore?" I asked a friend. "I really feel scared out there on the street. I can't figure it out. God knows, I've always done a lot of running around New York, but I don't know what's wrong with me, do you?" My friend didn't know either. "I guess it's because you're not working anywhere," she offered. "You probably ought to go on back to work." But I didn't feel up to doing that.

My shrink and I talked twice a week, while I worried about my dwindling funds. Nothing ever seemed to come out of our talks. Still, I needed his reassurance that I wasn't going nuts. It would just take time, he said, for me to feel all right again. After all, I'd had some really bad times with some really serious illnesses. It would indeed take time.

26.

Alan and I were together all the time now. Most nights I slept at his apartment, because my own seemed so menacing. I always felt safe with Alan. He let me snuggle up under his chin while he patted my back and said, "There, there, baby, it'll be all right." When he said that, I really believed it would be. But when Alan left for work and I was alone, I felt terribly, terribly afraid, though I wasn't sure of what. And when I went back to my own silent apartment, I just crawled into bed and listened to my heart beat.

Even at Alan's apartment my insomnia was getting worse. Alan was so concerned that it was his snoring that kept me awake that he gallantly moved to the sofa and gave up his bed. But I still couldn't sleep more than a couple of hours before I had to get up to take my second dose of Placidyl. One night, when I got up to do that, I fell to the floor with a thud. Alan rushed to help me to my feet, shouting, "What's happening? What are you doing?" And I said, "I'm going to take my sleeping pill." "My God, you *are* asleep!" "No, I need to take the sleeping pill." And before Alan could talk me out of it, I took it.

Alan found a man he thought would be the perfect agent for me. I put the book outline into his hands and prayed that this time there would be some positive results. My new agent asked me to give him a month or so to get things rolling.

I went back to the diet doctor and got back on the low-carbohydrate diet. Maybe this doctor had been right. Maybe his diet should be my permanent way of life. When he asked whether I was on any medication, I reeled off the list. "No wonder you're having problems!" he exploded. "I'm going to replace all those medicines with the proper vitamins." And so he prescribed the megadoses of different vitamins that had now become the newest diet sensation and he swore that they would not only make me calm but would cure my insomnia to boot. I took them all, along with the medications my doctor had given me (which I knew better than to give up), but I didn't feel any better. In fact some of those vitamins made me feel strange indeed, and I never did lose any weight.

I was concerned about my fears. Suddenly I was afraid to go anywhere alone. If I had to go out I took a taxi from my door to the door of my destination. Sometimes I even called a radio dispatched taxi, to make sure I had one waiting. I couldn't figure out what it was that I was so afraid of, and I chalked it up to the fact that I didn't belong anywhere now that I wasn't working. Everybody else was safely ensconced in an office. All my friends were busy all the time. I didn't feel safe floating around the streets of New York by myself, and so, most of the time, when I had made a luncheon date or appointment to meet someone, I cancelled at the last minute. I really didn't want to leave the apartment. It seemed so much trouble to go down thirty-six floors. Besides, I didn't want to miss my afternoon nap.

I was afraid of a lot of things by this time. The mail, for instance. I always felt sure the mail would have some unpleasant news, and I dreaded opening the box to see what was inside. Most of the time I didn't go near the mailbox for days. Finally my doorman would bring up great tied-up bundles of letters and papers. I tossed them onto the dining-room table, where they remained unopened.

I guessed that I was afraid the letters might be bills. Lack of money was becoming a prime cause of my fear.

I felt pretty sure my druggist was cheating me. My drug bill hovered at around four hundred dollars a month, and the pills seemed to disappear so quickly. When the vials arrived I would empty the tablets onto my bed and count them. To my surprise, there was always the right number, but they didn't seem to last any time at all. I began to worry when the bottle was half empty, and I usually refilled the prescription about then. I had to get a new prescription from my doctor every three times I filled it. My doctor said he trusted me and knew I was no addict but he did want to keep an eye on the number of refills, just to be sure.

I knew that if I had to, I could probably get some extra Valium from my shrink. For the moment, I didn't have to.

Neither my doctor nor I realized that I was exhibiting the addict's obsession with her drug supply. I assumed it was perfectly normal to worry about having enough Valium. I simply couldn't function without it.

Alan kept badgering me about taking so many pills, especially the sleeping pills. "You don't even give the damn thing time to work," he growled. "You've only been lying there five minutes. Wait, for God's sake!" But since I could tell by the flippity-flop of my heart that I wasn't going to be able to sleep, it made more sense to take an extra Valium than to toss and turn and work myself into a sweat. I silently resented Alan's chidings. After all, who was he to talk, anyway? When he couldn't sleep he took a slug of vodka. I couldn't do that. I *had* to rely on Valium and a sleeping pill.

Other people were surprised, too, when they saw me take out my silver pillbox. I had to admit it was pretty spectacularly stuffed. Occasionally one of the vials in my purse would lose its cap and send hundreds of pills rolling around the bottom of my handbag. It was embarrassing to have them tumble out onto the floor when I withdrew my wallet. People looked at me suspiciously, as if I were carrying around some sort of illicit drugs.

I kept badgering my doctor about my weight problem because nothing had helped that. I still weighed 112 pounds, which was way above my normal, comfortable weight. I was still swollen around the stomach in the most unattractive way, and I couldn't get my puffy feet into any kind of decent-looking shoes. The diuretics didn't seem to help at all, and the only thing the thyroid medicine did was make me more nervous and jumpy.

I was scared. I knew that something was very, very wrong inside my body. What was scarier yet, nobody seemed able to tell me what it was. Maybe, I thought, my thyroid had been permanently damaged. Certainly my metabolism seemed to be malfunctioning. I felt helpless and frenetic. I couldn't fight it anymore by myself and my doctor didn't seem to know what to do either. The more time that passed with no solution in sight, the more despondent I became.

That was it. Despondent. I thought, "If this is the way I have to live then I don't want to do it." I was so terribly tired of feeling sick. But I didn't quite have the nerve to kill myself, so I walked around the edges of life, not feeling much of anything save the pounding of my fearful heart, while I prayed to God, every single hour of every single day, that he would take me away from it all. But I didn't die. On the other hand, I wasn't living either.

My doctor said he knew a good endocrinologist—one who was willing to take the time and the trouble to look deeply into my problems. It would be a good idea for me to have the once-over from him, just so we would know, finally, what my seemingly gone-wild metabolic system was up to. Then we could fix it, for sure.

I was elated. It was the first ray of hope for a long time. After three days of tests, the endocrinologist gave me the results: "They are absolutely normal. Everything is functioning perfectly." He added, "But I think you are taking too many drugs. I want you to give up all those vitamins."

I felt stunned. Nothing was wrong with me after all. I was doomed and damned to lifelong inhabitation of a body running awry. There was absolutely nothing anybody could do about it.

"I'm just *not* going to give up my vitamins!" I told my doctor, "That's crazy."

"Of course not," he agreed, "that's ridiculous."

My mother called to tell me she'd discussed my problems with her own physician in Alabama. To her alarm, he had said, "Poor girl, they're going to kill her up there." She asked him what he meant. He said, "With all those pills." My mother was frightened. With a catch in her voice, she said, "Mary Ann, promise me you'll see another doctor or do something. I'm so worried about you."

I decided I'd better talk about it with my shrink. "Mary Ann, I think we ought to try to cut down the doses of Navane. I'm going to give you a prescription for just half the strength and we'll see how it works." He sent me out with the new prescription and the admonition to call him and let him know how I felt.

For a couple of days I tried to make do on that half-strength capsule, but everything looked as if I were seeing it in a funhouse mirror. I told my shrink I didn't think we ought to fool around with the Navane. After all, that seemed to be the only thing holding my head together. Without Navane, I felt quite mad.

My doctor felt concerned about the Placidyl I was taking. Maybe it wasn't doing the job anymore and that was why I had to take so much of it. He thought we ought to try one of the old-fashioned remedies, like chloral hydrate, so I added the little green perles to my multicolored collection of medicines. They seemed to work all right, but whenever they didn't put me to sleep fast enough, I took a Placidyl as well—and two or three Valium, maybe a phenobarbital, two Fiorinal, and on occasion a codeine tablet. If that didn't work, I used my grandmother's remedy—aromatic spirits of ammonia, one teaspoonful in a little water. That seemed to soothe me immediately. The bottles were tiny, and I ran through one a day. I was a little worried that the alcohol in the ammonia might be dangerous to my pancreas, but I figured it was safer than taking any higher dosage of Valium.

27.

Oh, my God, what's the matter with this bed? It's so hard. My back hurts so. I opened my eyes and stared at an unfamiliar ceiling. I saw, slightly out of focus, the little blue and white flowers of the dressing-room walls. I was lying on the floor.

A dagger of fear split my heart. Dear God, what am I doing here?

I tried to get up but I couldn't. I felt so terribly heavy. I rolled over and put my hand to my spine. It was so sore!

After what seemed an interminable time, I managed to pull myself onto my knees. I could not stand, so I crawled on my hands and knees into the bedroom. If I held on to the bed posts, maybe I could get myself into bed. Slowly, and with tremendous effort, I dragged myself onto the mattress and sank again into a very deep sleep.

The light woke me. I wasn't sure what had happened to me the night before. The soreness in my back nudged a tiny fragment of a memory. God! What was I doing on the floor? I began to sob.

Hours later, when I was finally able to get out of bed, I saw my spine was tattooed with big, ugly black-and-blue bruises. But I still couldn't remember what it was I had done to myself. All I could remember was getting ready for bed and taking my medicines.

I felt so weak. Exhausted. But I had slept, hadn't I?

I telephoned my doctor. What had happened to me? Was he sure I didn't have something wrong with my brain? Was I going to die? I began to cry in heaving, gasping, catches of breath. "Oh, God, what is wrong with me, can't you tell me what is wrong with me, what is happening? . . ." My doctor replied, "I don't know. Come in tomorrow and we'll see."

My shrink said he thought it was the Placidyl. "Sometimes, Mary Ann, these things react more quickly than usual. You probably just had one of those strange quick reactions to the Placidyl. That has to be it."

"But it couldn't be," I told him. "I had just that minute swallowed it."

Neither of my doctors mentioned convulsions, though that, of course, is what it had been.

My agent telephoned to talk to me about the book outline and tell me his plans for it. When we hung up I felt far more cheerful than I had in months. It looked as if this was my man after all. At least he was working on a sale. A few moments later, Alan called. "John asked me if you've been drinking. I told him you don't drink." I couldn't understand it at all. My agent already knew I couldn't drink. The publishing business must be getting to him. As it was to us all.

My friend Sarah kept saying, "Mary Ann, you do take too much medicine." We'd been discussing it for some time now, and I had told her that nobody seemed able to help me get off all the drugs, and I really was afraid to give up stuff like Navane. I had no idea what would happen to my mind without it. But Sarah persisted. "Listen, Mary Ann, I've met this doctor—he's setting up a clinic to help people get off pills. I'll take you to meet him if you want to go. Maybe he has some new treatment or something." And so on a lovely cool November day we took a taxi to the hospital across town where the doctor had his new office. "We'll go by subway," Sarah had insisted, "it's faster."

"No, I can't. We'll have to take a cab."

"But, Mary Ann, that will cost a fortune."

"No, Sarah I can't go on a subway. I'm afraid of subways."

The doctor, I decided, was just another hustling psychiatrist. He'd tried to railroad me into his clinic, and I wasn't having any of that. Not until I'd checked him out with my own two doctors. Anyway, I didn't like the way he talked. I sure as hell wasn't checking myself into any hospital over the Thanksgiving holiday, only a week away. Two weeks in the hospital with passes to go in and out. Screw it! I didn't need two weeks in the hospital.

I asked my shrink if he knew anything about this doctor's clinic. When he said he didn't, I closed the case, though I did thank Sarah profusely for her interest. I knew she was sincerely concerned.

Alan and I spent Thanksgiving with friends of his in Connecticut. Halfway through dinner, the husband, who'd been drinking, it seemed, since the night before, rose to give a toast and crashed to the floor. The festivities came to a screeching halt while the male members of the party carried the host upstairs to bed. The wife was humiliated and crying and she took me aside and said, "Can't you talk to him, Mary Ann? You gave up drinking. Can't you tell him how to do it?" I promised I would.

It was December, the end of another year. And we were going to sell a book. At last.

My agent was holding an auction. I should stay by the telephone until five in the afternoon. We'd know by then.

I took Valium every few hours. Alan came to hold my hand. He knew what I was feeling. He knew how important it was that we make this sale, not only for the sake of my career, but because I so desperately needed the money.

At five o'clock the call came. There had been no sale.

"I'm going to have a drink," I told Alan.

"Don't," he said.

"No, I'm going to." And I did.

It was the first time in ages I'd felt my heart slow down. Down to normal, down to quiet, down to sleep.

When I woke up, I remembered what I had done. The booze had felt the way I knew it would. Warm, reassuring, like a massage down the length of my gullet, relaxing all the tightened-up muscles. I wondered idly whether I was going to die. Well, I wasn't dead yet. I hadn't even gotten drunk—just calm. Yes, I was feeling good now. Relaxed. Quiet. Secure. Hopeful. Determined. Whole. Almost happy.

But then I remembered. The book. I hadn't sold the book. And I didn't know what I was going to do.

I called my doctor's office. "Do you really think just a tablespoonful would hurt me?" I asked his nurse. Booze seemed to be the answer to my sleeping problems. Since my first drink in six years hadn't killed me, I reasoned another wasn't going to. Still, I wanted to be sure. I didn't want pancreatitis again.

"Mary Ann, don't be ridiculous. A tablespoonful isn't going to do you any good. It's all psychological. Don't take the risk." I hung up the phone to ponder that. I didn't want to ask my doctor. He'd be furious for sure. But I knew the tablespoon of booze would help me sleep, so I decided to risk it after all.

It seemed as if every function of my body, by then, was operating by chemical means. Diuretics flushed my kidneys, and my bowels worked only when I used suppositories or laxatives. When both of those methods failed, I learned to extract the fecal material with my hand. I felt a certain sense of triumph that I could do that. Almost as if I were going to show my rebellious body that it could not beat me. I would make it work. Somehow.

My glands were regulated by medication. My muddled mind was kept on an even keel with Navane. Of course, I still took the Cogentin as a side-effect antidote, but it no longer relieved the stiffness in my hands that made my handwriting so illegible. I just didn't try to write anymore and communicated painfully and very slowly by typewriter.

I deadened all the aches and pains—from my headache to my often-tender tummy—with painkillers and deadened my mind with sleeping pills when the time came to let the body rest.

But I never felt rested at all and I continued to wonder just how long my body and I were going to survive in this medically automated life.

My menses had stopped. My gynecologist repeated his diagnosis of two years earlier. Menopause.

I began to believe that if I got away from New York for a while—to Alabama, of course—things would get better. I swore I'd stay there until everything was OK. Until my book had been sold.

My druggist had promised to mail my allotment of Valium. It was simpler, he said, than giving me the prescription copy and he didn't want to give me several months' supply all at once. But by the time I ran out of Valium, nothing had come by mail. When I telephoned the druggist he said, "Oh, gee, I'm so sorry, everything has been so hectic." I heard myself shouting, "What do you expect me to do? Get somebody over to the post office today and send it airmail, special delivery, and if there's any problem, call me back collect. I am really *furious!* I counted on you to do what you promised."

One of my old high-school classmates was a dentist. He could get me thirty Valium—just enough to last until the package arrived from New York. I cautioned him not to let my father know—I'd go pick up the package from the druggist myself. My father was funny that way.

The longer I stayed in Alabama, the less likely it seemed that the book would get sold. So I went back to New York.

The city seemed friendlier than when I'd left, and I decided that '78 would be a very good year. Even my apartment seemed cozy, perhaps because now it wasn't so deadly quiet. In fact, it was just a mite too noisy. The Arabs next door were in residence, and tribes of djellabahed types marched in and out in a file. I didn't know who they were, but they sure were noisy. Some nights every pill in my collection didn't help me sleep. Nor did the tablespoonful or two of booze I allowed myself.

After a couple of weeks, I decided nothing much had changed. Things still weren't OK. I still didn't want to go out. Every morning I looked over my calendar and systematically cancelled all engagements.

One night the Arabs had another party, this time with full orchestra. Damn! I have to get my sleep. If I don't sleep I'm going to die. I know I am. I just can't survive. My heart pounded, as the blood seemed to leave my body and I shivered and shook with the cold. For the next three hours I continued to swallow Valium. And then I took all three sizes of Placidyl at once.

When the table fell on me, and glass crashed around me, and the cuts began to bleed and the bruises began to hurt, I knew what I had done. I had come full circle in my life. I was back where I had begun. I was drunk.

It was February. It was snowy. I was sick. Again. I felt so terrible. God!

I took all my pills and for days I lay in my bed and I did not get well. Then one day none of them helped. I cried and cried until my eyes were red and swollen and I couldn't breathe anymore. I knew I just couldn't go on anymore.

That night, when I was about to take all my medicines, I looked down, saw the rainbow of pills, and knew that in my hand I held the instrument of my death.

I dropped the pills and sobbed into Alan's shoulder, "You have to help me. Somebody has to help me."

Alan went to the telephone and I heard him say, to someone I did not know, "Jenny, listen, I think you can help me . . . I have a friend, she's been taking a lot of pills. . . ." The rest of what he said was unintelligible over the sound of my sobs.

"She says she'll arrange for you to see her doctor tomorrow. She says you must go. It can't wait."

"Who?"

"Someone I've known for years. She's an alcoholism counselor at Roosevelt Hospital. Funny, I never thought of her before. She says she can help you."

That was how the nightmare ended. And that was how a different sort of nightmare began. A nightmare that would, ultimately, give me back my life.

II.

28.

"Damn these doctors!" Dr. Zuckerman swore, "I'm sorry, but I get o damned mad. They really should know better."

I sat shivering on the examining table, nude beneath the obscenely ackless, thin white robe, while a total stranger pushed and probed at ny body. "How did you happen to be taking all of that stuff?" he con- nued, while I explained what all my medications were for. Pancrea- tis. Thyroiditis. Migraines. Anxiety. Pain. Fear.

I was in the office of Dr. Harold Zuckerman, a man I didn't know at ll, and I was just about to put my life in his hands. I didn't see that I ad any choice. Not anymore.

Dr. Zuckerman practiced at Roosevelt Hospital, where he worked losely with the alcoholism rehabilitation unit there—Smithers. It was here Jenny worked. Now he was saying, "I want you in the hospital."
"When?"
"Today."
The tears stung my eyelids and I felt colder than ever.
"I can't possibly go to the hospital today. I have things to do."

"Then tomorrow. My nurse will arrange it. The hospital will call yo for confirmation."

As he prepared to dismiss me he said one last thing: "Bring all you medicines with you."

"Everything?"

"Every single thing in your medicine cabinet."

And he then sent me home.

I knew the end had come. The end of my life as it had been and th beginning of my life as it would be. The end of sedated calm, the begin ning of I-didn't-know-what terrors. The end of pills and the beginnin of withdrawal.

Withdrawal was something I knew about. After all, hadn't I see enough movies? Cold sweats, pain, agony. The fact was I didn't real know. Not yet.

I went home alone with my fear. Was it going to hurt a lot? Woul they wrap me in sheets? Tie my hands down? Would I be able to tak it?

I had never been so afraid. My body felt like a thing removed fro reality, far removed from me. My brain seemed to be floating some where else, watching me. At home I cried and longed for Alan's arms t comfort me. But there was to be no comfort for a long, long time.

I telephoned my mother and we both cried. I telephoned my fathe who said he was relieved; he would fly to New York if I needed him. needed him.

Then I told my friends. All offered their support and their love an never have friends been as important as mine were on that day.

I didn't know what else to do, so I got my hair cut. It seemed logica get beautiful for the kill. If I was, in fact, going to die, I might as we die looking my best. The truth was it would get my mind off what didn't want to face. Tomorrow. I might as well face tomorrow lookin good.

I wasn't looking good, though. In the mirror at the hairdresser's I sa myself—pale, old, ugly. Addiction is never pretty, and my own addictio was showing.

Back home, alone in my apartment, I felt the fear creeping up m throat, cutting off my breath, racing through my heart. I took a Valiun

There were a hundred details to take care of before I disappeare into the bowels of Roosevelt Hospital. I didn't know when I'd get out.

didn't even know *if* I'd get out. I had no idea at all what fate might be lurking for me there.

Alan came to stay with me until morning, but the fear that lay hard and heavy on my heart did not leave me.

I packed. I knew I was packing all the wrong things, but I couldn't seem to get it right. Clothes, but where were my nightgowns? Snow boots, but what would I do for a robe? I made a mental note to buy some respectable underwear. When I got out. I looked inside the medicine cabinet, but I didn't pack the pills. Not yet. Then I lay in Alan's arms and waited for sleep.

But sleep never came, in spite of the usual doses of Placidyl, Valium, and Fiorinal. In a panic I took everything I thought might make me sleep. Phenobarbital, chloral hydrate, more and more Valium. Until, at last, blessed oblivion.

When morning came I almost wished it hadn't, for now I had to face the fear that was inside me, the nightmare within that was emerging a reality.

I wanted my daddy. I wanted to be a child again, a child that someone would hold and reassure that everything would be all right. I wanted someone else to feel all this for me.

My brain reverberated with the screams of all the movie junkies I had ever seen going cold turkey, suffering agonies I could not imagine. What would that agony be like? Would there be much pain? Would I convulse? Could I stand it? Would Alan be waiting for me when and if I ever came out? Could he stand seeing me as I was—ill, ugly, and addicted? Would he ever love me again? Did he love me now?

The fear sat like a stone inside my stomach and shook like a leaf on my ice-cold hands.

Alan had gone, and I was alone once more with that fear that kept me company while I roamed through the house, waiting for the telephone call that was to summon me to the hospital.

I took my day's allotment of pills—the vitamins, Navane, pancreas pills, digestive pills, diuretics, thyroid pills, and a Valium for good measure. As long as the hospital and Dr. Zuckerman were going to get me off pills, let them deal with it. For now, I'd have to take the things I knew would keep me ambulatory until I got there.

And I wouldn't pack the pills yet. I'd wait for the hospital call.

I paced the floor of the apartment, looking around to memorize every detail, while my skin crawled and the nerves tingled beneath. I wanted to go now and get the whole damned thing over with. But I also wanted to stay at home and forget the whole damned thing.

The telephone shrilled. It was the hospital. "Be here in an hour."

Trembling, I hurried about the apartment, checking drawers, filling suitcases, trying to remember all I must do, while the second hand swept round and round the clock, erasing the few minutes I had left.

Finally, I emptied the medicine cabinet of everything from razor blades to vitamins to toothpaste to sedatives, until it was completely bare. I stood staring. I had never seen it that way before.

The razor blades and toothpaste went into my cosmetics kit. There was another suitcase I'd reserved for the pills. It was 11 inches by 16 inches by 6 inches. It was full. It was heavy. And it was all pills.

I got myself into the one pair of pants that would fit over my swollen stomach, shoved my feet into heavy boots (New York was burrowing out of a blizzard), pulled on my storm coat and left my home and my life as it was, behind.

I was not alone this time. Alan was by my side. Together we dragged my suitcases and sloshed through the snow, into a cab and, all too quickly, into Roosevelt Hospital.

It was February 24, 1978. A Friday.

29.

Roosevelt is one of the least oppressive hospitals I know. I'd been there the previous spring for my eyelid operation, so Roosevelt held less hospital-terrors than most. If I had to go to a hospital, at least this one wasn't so bad.

After the usual wait while hospital red tape wound itself around me, Alan and I were led to my room, a pleasant one in the private patient ward. Thank God Dr. Zuckerman had kept me out of the alcoholic ward; at least my ordeal would be endured in relative privacy. Privacy, it turned out, was not Dr. Zuckerman's reason. The alcoholic ward would keep patients for only five days. He knew my withdrawal would take longer.

I would have a roommate, of course—at least I would if I wanted the insurance company to pay—but I didn't mind that. They say roommates help healing go faster, and that's what I wanted—to get it over with as fast as possible, so I could resume my life.

The woman in the bed next to mine looked a whole lot sicker than I. She'd had an operation to remove her thyroid gland and she was waiting for the verdict on her biopsy. She couldn't speak above a whisper and she looked in a hell of a lot of pain, but she was cheery, and that helped, even though there was no way on earth I was going to feel cheered. I was terribly, terribly scared. I put on my nightgown and climbed into bed to wait. Alan pulled up a chair. Dr. Zuckerman appeared almost immediately and began his examination. It was a thorough one: blood pressure, electrocardiogram, blood samples, reflex tests, lights shined in my eyes, and on and on and on. When he had finished, he gave me something to do: unpack the pills and arrange them by categories—vitamins, tranquilizers, painkillers, etc. That would keep me occupied until he got back. He disappeared again.

Alan and I spent the next fifteen minutes sorting pills, bottle after colorful bottle. There were the pancreas pills and the thyroid pills and the antihistamines and the pills to ward off side effects from other pills. Then there were the painkillers and the tranquilizers and the sleeping pills in multiples. Everything, in fact, was in multiples, and seeing row after row of them lined up the length of the six-foot windowsill was sobering indeed. My roommate watched, dumbfounded. I didn't know how to explain, so I didn't try.

A resident appeared, took one look, drew in his breath and whistled, and disappeared. Dr. Zuckerman came back and, without a word, swept all the bottles into a large paper bag and took them all away. Goodbye, babies. Farewell, friends. Hello, panic.

I didn't cry. The tears were terror-frozen somewhere deep down inside. In fact, tears were not to come for a very long time. With unseeing eyes, I kissed Alan goodbye, and waited, trembling, for the end of this life to happen.

The action began. Two nurses appeared, one with a blood-pressure machine, the other with an enormous needle. I turned up my rear end to receive two incredibly painful shots. "Vitamins," I was told. I found out later they were huge doses of vitamin B, standard treatment for alcoholics and addicts. The medications nurse appeared with a capsule. "Take your Librium." But I didn't associate the green and white of this capsule with the green and black Librium I'd tried, and been allergic to, years before. I supposed (correctly) that it was stronger stuff. I found out later it was 25 milligrams, and I was to take one every four hours. It was the beginning of my detoxification. For the next few days I would be watching that Librium closely, looking for a change in the color that would mean the dosage was going down and the chance of serious withdrawal symptoms was going up. But for the moment I just swallowed the Librium and waited. Within half an hour I was, once again, sedative-calm. Suddenly hospitalization didn't seem half-bad.

When the nurses had gone, my roommate and I got acquainted. I told her about my addiction, which was hardly necessary in view of the pills that had lined the windowsill. She told me about her work in the methadone clinic of Roosevelt Hospital (odd coincidence, I thought). As we chattered I realized I was feeling more alive than I had in weeks. Was it because at last someone was *doing something* for me? Or was it simply the 25 milligrams of Librium?

There was a terrible dinner of some sort—dried-out fish, as I recall— and I spent some time amusing myself filling out menus for the next few days. I really didn't feel very hungry.

Then there were more capsules, two more painful shots and a visit from the resident doctor. The resident was a girl-child, tiny, dark, and beautiful, who looked to be about twenty-three at the most. It was difficult to call her Dr. Rosenblum. She gave me the same thorough once-over Dr. Zuckerman had: she tested my eyes, blood pressure, my heart, and my hands for tremors. It was a routine she would be repeating every day for quite a while.

Finally, the day had gone and dinner had gone and visitors had gone and tests had gone and night had come. My roommate gave herself up easily to sleep. I waited. And waited. But sleep didn't come. I did not know then that sleep would not come at all for nearly a week.

I had never believed I would die from pills, but was always sure that I would die without sleep. Sleep was to be gotten at any cost, and fear of not sleeping was what sent all those sleeping pills down my gullet. But for one week in Roosevelt Hospital, I did not sleep. And I did not die.

It sounds like an exaggeration. Despite the claim "I never closed my eyes all night," most insomniacs sleep more than they care to admit. But I had witnesses to the fact that I did not. I marched restlessly up and down the halls all night long, and every four hours I reminded the medications nurse about my Librium, in hopes that it would do the job of putting me out. The Librium came; the sleep did not. The hands on the clock in the hall flew around like a speeded-up film. It was midnight, then one, two, three, four, and five o'clock. Morning again, I had closed my eyes all right, but I hadn't slept. By six, the hospital was awake and moving. I got up, washed my face, and took my first long look in the mirror. Staring back at me was a pair of eyes popped wide in—horror? terror? surprise? Where before they had been droopy-lidded and sleepy, now I could see the whites of my eyeballs all around, top and bottom. It gave me a fearsome, frightened look, a look I'd have for the next two weeks.

30.

During that first morning in Roosevelt Hospital, I continued to feel it wasn't such a bad place to be. Hospital routines are pretty predictable, but at least Roosevelt's seemed to be more humane than most. For one thing, they brought us early-morning coffee. I greedily downed the whole carafe and settled contentedly back to await breakfast. Breakfast, of course, was the typical hospital mush, so I picked at my food and drank another two cups of coffee. Suddenly my heart began to race, and I wondered whether I might be having a heart attack. My hands trembled, and I felt weak and shaky. My skin began to crawl in a way I'd never felt before—almost as if all the nerve endings had suddenly been exposed. (It was a sensation that would become all too familiar in the months to come.)

Just then Dr. Zuckerman came by on his rounds. I showed him my shaking hands and told him about the four cups of coffee, and his answer was "That's four hundred milligrams of caffeine! What did you expect?" My coffee, from that day on, was limited to two cups per day. I'd learned an important lesson in stimulation. I'd never even realized caffeine was a drug.

Dr. Rosenblum came and did her usual battery of tests. Pills came, but the vitamin shots were gone for good. I continued to feel calm, wide-awake and relatively secure. My father would soon be here. My father was reality. My father was safety. My father was love. My father would make everything all right.

He and Alan had never met, and I didn't know what to expect when they did. Alan drank, my father didn't. Alan thought all I needed was a different shrink; my father believed I needed a hospital. Alan thought I just lacked will power; my father thought I needed help. I knew I needed help.

I telephoned my favorite bookstore and ordered stacks of trashy novels, to be delivered to the hospital. I felt I should settle in for a long winter's stay. Physically, so far, I felt remarkably well. Except for my scary, stary eyes, I looked pretty good, too, and I thought that my stomach had shrunk a bit. But it could be my imagination. Or perhaps the inedible food. I would watch it anyway. Wouldn't it be wonderful if my swollen stomach finally deflated?

When my father arrived he looked terribly tired and pale, and there were dark circles beneath his eyes. I was convinced a nap was what he needed. Coming from Alabama to New York and its slush had been a shock to his system. I could not know, of course, that the shock to my father's system was what had become of his little girl. He hid that from me beautifully.

My father and Alan sized each other up, politely though warily, and retired to the hall to talk. I knew that they would never agree on a thing. Not about my treatment. I knew that they would be pulling me back and forth between them, one arguing help, the other arguing strength. I just couldn't argue at all. I had given up. My life was completely in Roosevelt Hospital's hands. And Dr. Zuckerman's.

That first Saturday together, Alan and my father spelled stays with me. I didn't want to be alone, since I didn't know when something terrible—like sudden withdrawal symptoms—might begin. So far I was still feeling incredibly good—energetic, in fact. I didn't discover until much later that all the energy I felt wasn't real energy at all but simply the removal of the drugs. A sort of "simulated energy." But it felt good, and, for now, I felt calm. The withdrawal I dreaded had not come. Not yet.

I had a visitor—a stranger who appeared and announced that she would return at seven that evening to escort me to an AA meeting. No one asked whether I needed or wanted an AA meeting. An AA meeting

—any meeting, for that matter—was the very last thing I wanted. My spirit may have been willing, but my body *was* weak. In fact, walking was an experience in shape-warp, with walls falling away from my hands when I needed them there. Floors pitched like the decks of ships and my eyesight was blurred. Going to a meeting didn't seem like such a good idea, but that was what I was expected to do. (Somewhere wheels had turned and I had become caught up in the gears of Smithers, the alcoholic treatment unit of Roosevelt Hospital.)

At seven o'clock on the dot, my escort appeared at my door, and, in the company of my dad (families were invited), I set off to begin my in-hospital addiction therapy. AA, it seemed, was going to be part of my treatment.

The big conference room was hot, and filled with people—some, like me, in hospital robes and slippers. I sat with my father as far in the rear as possible, the better to make a hurried exit the moment I could escape. The speaker droned on and on, and I was miserable, with my skin crawling in that prickly, pins-and-needles way that I was beginning to accept as my lot. I couldn't see very well. All of a sudden my vision grew cloudy, as if a smoke screen had blown in front of my eyes. And then, just as suddenly, it cleared. No, it wasn't the smoke in the room; it was my eyes. One minute I felt like fainting, the next like throwing up. And the more I heard of the speaker's story, the more depressed I grew. (My father, on the other hand, sat in rapt attention.) When there was a break for coffee, I begged off, saying I felt too sick to stay. On my father's arm, I made a slow, shaky exit. Once back in my room, I crawled gratefully into bed. My first "trip" out had served only to show me how truly awful I felt.

The meeting, plus the effort of being out of bed for an hour, had exhausted me, and I felt sure I would be able to sleep at last. I did not, and night ran into day once more.

The next morning, my anonymous female visitor called and asked how I liked the meeting. Without thinking, I said, "I hated it." There was a moment's silence, then "I'll be there this evening at seven." They weren't going to let me off the hook. AA was required therapy throughout my hospital stay.

For the next couple of days my father visited every morning and Alan came every afternoon. When I was lucky, I had them both at once. When they had gone I tried to snuggle up with my trashy novels, but I discovered I couldn't read. My eyes simply didn't focus, and I saw everything through a haze. Type was squiggly, and I couldn't make out the words at all. I had to put the novels aside for the first few days.

When the weekend was over, my father had to leave, and my courage was going with him. As long as he was there, I felt protected, secure, as if everything would be all right. Now I just didn't know. I felt scared. Alone. Desolate. A little desperate. But my father had to go. I could see that. The trip had exacted a brutal toll, and the dark circles under his eyes now looked like purple scars. Still, I felt so scared being all alone.

By Monday I still hadn't slept. Days seemed endless. Friends telephoned and came to visit, but visits weren't any fun. I was having terrible visual disturbances, and I saw everyone with huge heads atop tiny little bodies. I couldn't tell my friends what I saw. It would scare them to death. They would think I was crazy after all. *Was* I crazy? But Dr. Rosenblum said it was all part of my drug withdrawal. (Had that started?) It wouldn't last. And so I continued to see everyone as if through the wrong end of a long telescope, and I was never really sure I wasn't simply losing my mind.

My mind was, in fact, taking a beating. Where was its Valium? Its Placidyl? Its Percodan and Fiorinal? Although the doctors had not yet begun to wean me off the Librium by lowering the dosage, my mind was already feeling the removal of its multi-medicinal crutch. It was reacting mightily to the lack of sedation. It was in overdrive, and the effects on my senses were weird and scary. One day I found myself going into a closet instead of the bathroom. My orientation was completely out of whack.

It happened. My Librium capsule was no longer the green and white I had come to expect. It was now green and black. That meant phased withdrawal from drugs had begun in earnest, and my life would either begin with it, or it would end. I had nothing to do except wait.

In that Land of No-Nod, where sleepless night swept into sleepless day and back to sleepless night again, life was a jumble, not of sense, but of senses. Today, in my relatively ordered life, I find it impossible to set those days down in sequence. I can remember only isolated events, and I can describe them only the way I remember them, not necessarily the way they happened.

I remember that Dr. Zuckerman came every day, right on schedule. Every day I panicked that he might not come; every day he did. There were always the same tests. I followed a pencil with my eyes (I never

knew that my eyes were rolling around uncontrollably in their sockets).
I applied pressure against his hands—the test for tremors. (Miraculously, true tremors never appeared.) My blood pressure, reflexes,
chest, heart and stomach were all checked each day, and—another miracle—they all checked out fine. Every morning Dr. Rosenblum came to
recheck everything herself. Other doctors came and went and checked
some more. I didn't know what all that checking was for then, though I
do now: they were watching for convulsions.

Dr. Zuckerman sent an ear, nose, and throat man to see me, in order
to find out what sort of damage I'd done with years of indiscriminate
nasal-spray use. I was complaining that I just couldn't do without my
nasal spray, that I couldn't breathe; I was going to suffocate. After all,
I'd depended on nasal sprays all my life.

But Dr. Zuckerman was telling me I might not have a functional nose
for the rest of my life, not if I continued to spray; maybe not in any
case. Such sprays are so deadly to nasal membranes that they can produce a permanently runny nose. Perhaps I'd already messed up my
membranes beyond repair.

The ENT man came to my room straight from the operating room,
wearing a comical-looking green surgical cap and floppy slippers. He
peered and probed and then announced that—(one more miracle) my
nose was still intact. He left me some oily drops that supposedly would
help me breathe without doing any damage. They never seemed to do
the job, though, so I finally developed my own technique. I sniffed
water from the faucet up my nose.

I acquired a "counselor." Like the AA escort, she simply appeared in
my room one day, introduced herself, and proceeded to ask me questions from an official-looking questionnaire. I had no idea where she
came from.

My counselor informed me that I was to attend a lecture on this day,
an AA meeting that night, a movie some other time. I complained that I
didn't feel well enough. "Be there," she said. I went.

The lecture was attended by patients in hospital gowns and robes—
all, like myself, recovering from addiction. Some had been brought into
the emergency room after an overdose, others had checked themselves
into the alcoholism ward. Some looked so out of it I didn't even ask
them. We sat in an overheated room and heard about the horrors of
booze and drug abuse. Brain damage. Nerve damage. Death. All of us
felt depressed and uncomfortable. They were talking about what might

have happened to us. All of us looked pretty terrible, too. We shook visibly and walked unsteadily. And we all felt relieved when it was over and we were escorted back to our rooms.

There was to be another AA meeting—this one for hospital patients only. The speaker was a young black man with a blood-curdling story. He'd been on booze, he'd been on drugs, he'd been a bookie, a junkie, and a thief. He'd tried to murder his wife and he'd done time. Yet here he was, looking sharp and sounding sane. I was impressed. He was the first AA person I'd been able to relate to. Was AA getting to me after all?

The Librium changed color once more—now it was green and yellow and only 5 milligrams—and I braced myself for what I knew would come. It came. Within hours I began to experience uncontrollable twitching in my hands and feet. I lay in bed and watched my arm leap up as if it had had an electric shock. I held it down on the bed with my other arm and prayed my roommate hadn't seen. The arm seemed a thing alive and not attached at all to me.

When I walked the halls, I did so gingerly, for the floor now rose and then fell away, and I never knew whether I was about to step off into some unseen abyss. I held on to the walls, and sometimes I called for help.

My eyes barely focused. Reading was impossible. So was signing my name. Dr. Zuckerman thought my handwriting looked OK, but I knew it was not my own.

Without sleep, nights were endless. My roommate slept peacefully through TV movies while I moaned helplessly, my body twitching as if on wires. By morning I was always exhausted.

Then, one night, something wonderful happened. I settled down to try, once more, to read one of the novels. This one was about the fashion industry, and it supposedly had juicy tidbits about some of my co-workers, thinly disguised. I turned on the reading light and tried to focus my eyes. If I blinked often enough, I could just make out the words.

The book was incredibly bad, but it was also funny and gossipy and gloriously scandalous, and the names that were changed to protect the innocent (or the author) didn't fool me a bit. I savored every item. After a while I closed my eyes—and woke up half an hour later. *I had slept!* Glory be, I had slept! I turned out the light and snuggled under the blankets, confident that my long, wakeful ordeal was over.

It was not. I did not sleep again for three more nights.

Alan was incredibly patient. Whenever I couldn't sleep, I telephoned him. Occasionally I woke him up. I didn't mean to be so selfish, but I was just scared. Surely if I didn't sleep I would die. But Alan always calmed me down and soothed me and said, in that wonderful low voice of his, "Just lie there and close your eyes. Just rest. It's almost as good for you. That's one thing I've learned from insomnia." I didn't believe a word, but I was willing to do whatever he suggested.

Alan and I had talked for a while in the dark one night while my roommate slept peacefully in her bed. When I put down the phone I closed my eyes. I awoke two hours later. It was my very first sustained sleep, the most I would have for a while, but it was the beginning of the return of a normal sleep pattern—a pattern I had destroyed with sleeping pills. At last there was hope. At last I felt I might survive after all.

Almost a week had gone by, and Dr. Zuckerman felt the time had come to run some tests on me, so that any myths about my physical condition could be dispelled once and for all. He and I didn't agree about my health. He didn't believe I'd ever had pancreatitis at all; I insisted I'd seen the lab reports. Not only that, I was terribly worried that going without my pancreas medication might send me back to square one of that disease, terrible pain and all. And so Zuckerman would do a battery of tests using the newest equipment, to try to determine the condition of my pancreas, liver, and, for good measure, entire gastrointestinal tract. The GI series again. My heart sank at the mention of that, and I had flashbacks of the blood in the radiologist's sink. "Nonsense," said Zuckerman, "there's no reason on earth why twelve hours without food or drink should cause any nausea. It's all your imagination. You'll have to get over that." But I wasn't reassured, and the closer it came, the more frightened I felt.

At midnight the nurses came and removed the water pitcher from beside my bed, depositing a "Nothing By Mouth" sign in its place. That made me crave water. I tried to put it out of my mind, but my mouth was dry and uncomfortable and my heart was racing out of control. What would happen to me this time? I walked the halls as the hour for my Librium came and went. "Nothing By Mouth" the sign said.

I lay down on my bed but my body was trembling and my head had begun to ache. The bed seemed like an enemy and I tossed and turned and heard myself moan. My roommate heard me moan, too, and moved in her painful sleep, as I tried to muffle what were, by now, screams.

As dawn broke, I was bathed in cold sweat, holding my head, which pounded with unspeakable, brutalizing pain. I just couldn't lie down. I would wash my hair. That's what I'd do. Wash my hair. Maybe the hot water would help.

For a moment, it did, but the pain returned quickly and I continued to pace the floor, up and down, trying to hold it off. A nurse came in with a wheelchair to take me to X-ray. We made it only as far as the elevator. There I threw up, great racking heaves while the wheelchair was thrust into the elevator and plummeted into the depths of the hospital. I vomited into a pan as we navigated twisted, turning corridors where torture-chamber equipment stood in rows. Everybody along our route stared as I held my head, moaned and continued to throw up. We made it as far as Nuclear Medicine. I was going to have a sonogram done of my innards. The vomiting subsided long enough for me to crawl up onto what appeared to be an X-ray table. A technician greased my stomach all over ("Buttered up for the kill," I said to myself) and rolled a little wheel over my stomach while she discussed my guts with her assistant. "There's the pancreas. Can you see the liver?" I didn't want to see. The sonogram was painless, but not fast enough. The moment they'd finished, I threw up again. Could they X-ray my stomach? No, they could not. They would have to wait. The floor nurse came for me, and, gently wiping my sweaty hair from my face, rolled me back to my room. She helped me into bed and someone brought me a heating pad for my head.

Suddenly I knew. This was withdrawal. This was what it was like. They'd taken away the drugs too soon! I rang frantically for the nurse. "Get Dr. Zuckerman, please!" The cry faded away into sobs. A nurse came in, running. "Please, please, call Dr. Zuckerman, I hurt so much!" I vomited again. "God, please, my head, please, you've got to do something." I vomited again. And I moaned, and cried and writhed there on my bed of pain.

Someone administered a suppository. Compazine, they told me. Someone else brought a Librium. This time it was green and white—back to full strength.

Somebody had told me my body would fight like hell to get the drugs it needed. Now I was discovering what hell felt like. I was terrified that my vision was permanently damaged. Everything seemed to be seen through cheesecloth. But young Dr. Rosenblum pronounced my eyes "better."

"Better? How? I can't see anything, Dr. Rosenblum. Am I going blind? What do you mean, better?"

"They've stopped rolling around," was the reply. I held the heating pad to my head and for two hours I hurt. More Librium.

Within a half hour after the second dose of Librium, my body gave up the fray and the pain and vomiting stopped. But I felt deeply depressed. I was right back where I had begun. Heavily tranquilized.

Dr. Zuckerman appeared and confirmed my suspicions about what had happened. He simply hadn't realized I was still so firmly hooked. I'd just been through a severe withdrawal episode. ("So *that's* what it's like?") We'd have to wait a day or so and try the whole X-ray procedure again. "I want to be absolutely sure about you physically," said Zuckerman. "I want you to see you don't need any medication. For anything."

But for now I would get Librium every four hours.

The next doses of Librium were green and black again—10 milligrams. They were trying, once more, to detoxify me for good. The doctor in charge of the detoxification unit of the hospital—a man with a reputation as the best in his specialized business—came to visit and quizzed me on the types and amounts of medicines I'd been taking. He left, shaking his head and looking puzzled. Later Dr. Zuckerman told me why: "With you it's like trying to divide apples by oranges." Nobody knew the best way to wean me from drugs.

It was decided, finally, that I would get phenobarbital, but not in pill form. It would be disguised in orange juice, the better to fool my subconscious into believing I hadn't had a pill at all. The theory was that pills themselves became their own *raison d'être,* and that anything with a little round shape might set off a bell in my brain that rang "Goodie! Drugs!" I didn't go along with the theory. My own addiction, I knew, was not to the shape of the pills but to the effect. No matter. I still got phenobarb in orange juice until I gagged; then I got it in tomato juice.

Phenobarbital had never been my drug of choice. It always made me feel so drugged. I had taken phenobarbital only when the thought of too many Valium frightened me. And this phenobarb was making me feel rotten. Not nice and relaxed like the Librium. Rotten.

And so on Saturday, after eight days of hospitalization, I told Dr. Zuckerman I didn't want any more phenobarbital. My detoxification was over. We waited twenty-four watchful hours to be sure I wouldn't suffer any more severe withdrawal symptoms. And then I was free from drugs. Free at last. Forever.

But I wasn't free from their effects. I wouldn't have drugs out of m
system for six more months.

We tried for the GI series once more, and this time (I could hardl
believe it) I passed the nothing-by-mouth test with little more than hun
ger pangs. Hallelujah!

Dr. Zuckerman brought the results to show me—pancreas fine
liver fine; in fact my insides were absolutely normal. The thyroi
checked out fine. I was healthy! Healthy? Me? Yes, healthy. I had abso
lutely no need for any medicines. No organic need, that is. The addic
tive need hadn't left me yet. That, in fact, was the only physical diseas
I had—the disease of addiction. I was going to have that for the rest o
my natural life. But together we would hold it in remission.

Smithers swung into action, and I discovered that the alcoholisn
treatment center was now in charge of my life. My counselor appeare
and told me I couldn't go home. "What are you saying, I can't g
home?"

"You know you can't, Mary Ann. You can't possibly do this b
yourself. You'll have to go to our rehab."

"Rehab? What's that?"

"A place where they'll take care of you for the next month. A plac
to recover, where you can get the treatment you need."

Well, I wasn't going. I was going home. I wanted Alan. I wanted my
apartment, Arab noise and all. I wanted to get out of there. I'd done it
I'd gotten through the withdrawal. Now I wanted to go home.

But somewhere, deep in my heart, I knew I couldn't go home. I knew
that, even with Alan's help, I just didn't feel up to fending for myself. I
knew I wanted to be taken care of. By somebody.

"That's ridiculous," Alan argued. "You just need a better shrink
You're perfectly capable of taking care of yourself. There isn't a thing
wrong with you now."

"You've got to remember, Alan drinks," said Dr. Zuckerman
"You'll be taken care of at the rehab . . . it's just like going back t
school. Everybody loves it. You'll meet lots of new people."

I was getting scared. Suddenly, those in charge of my life were send
ing me "away." "Away" meant some unknown place, with some un
known people, to an unknown life. And the unknown was scary. But I
didn't know whom to believe—Alan, or Dr. Zuckerman and the counse-

lor? Or my own divided heart? Part of me wanted home and Alan. The other wanted someone to take care of me.

Suddenly I knew I just couldn't face my apartment. Not the isolated thirty-sixth floor with the noisy Arabs. No, I just couldn't face that right now.

"Don't worry," said the counselor, "you're going to love the rehab center. It's a big, beautiful mansion. You'll make friends for life— everybody there does—and when you come out you're going to look like a new person. You're really not going to want to leave."

I didn't believe her at all.

As my discharge day approached, suddenly no place on earth seemed as secure and wonderful as Roosevelt Hospital. No patient had ever wanted to stay as badly as I did. At least Roosevelt was a known quantity. I didn't know anything at all about Smithers.

Was this what it felt like to be sent to jail? The more I thought about being incarcerated, restrained, in a place I didn't even know, with people that were—God knows what—the faster my heart beat, the more my arms jerked, the more my stomach flopped and flipped.

I got an unexpected reprieve. "Have you been sleeping?" asked the counselor.

"No. Well, one or two hours a night."

"Oh, they don't want you at Smithers yet, then." Thank God! I could relax in Roosevelt for two more days. I'd go there on Monday. It would have been ten long days since I was admitted to Roosevelt Hospital.

I prayed that the weekend would be a long one. That night, to my surprise, I slept. Four hours in one night! The counselor was delighted. That would do for a Smithers beginning.

"We'll transfer you up there in an ambulette."

"Like hell you will. I'm going home."

"You can't go home."

"Watch me!"

OK, I had to go to Smithers. But I'd be damned if I was going anywhere without going home first. I had things to do. For one thing, I needed clothes. They didn't wear nightgowns in Smithers, they'd said: "Bring your jeans." (Could I get into my jeans? I wondered, as I checked out my discernibly flatter tummy.) I had to check up on the mail (this time I'd even open it), get some money, see how my apartment looked. Most of all, I needed some time with Alan. I wanted, desperately, to have Alan make love to me. I needed to feel he still loved me. I needed to show him I loved him. Most of all, I needed to feel alive again. Like a woman again.

I won. The counselor and Dr. Zuckerman reluctantly agreed to a four-hour gap between Roosevelt release and Smithers admission. But I couldn't go home alone. Who was going to be with me? Alan, naturally.

"No, you can't go with him."

"What do you mean, I can't go with Alan?"

"He drinks. Suppose he takes you to a bar?"

I couldn't believe my ears. They saw Alan as the enemy. Alan as the person who would provide me with drugs or booze. Alan as my downfall. It was my very first glimpse of the paranoia that surrounds Smithers. (A protective paranoia, I discovered much later.)

But I won this round, too. Alan could take me home tomorrow. I had just four hours, not a minute more.

I shivered all night that Sunday, the panic forcing my breath out in short little puffs. I had to think of a way to get out of this set-up. I needed time to think. I had to plan. I had to arrange.

Then suddenly it was Monday and I was saying good-bye to my roommate, good-bye to all my nurses, good-bye to my counselor, and for the moment, good-bye to Dr. Zuckerman. I was on my way home. For four precious hours.

The four hours flew like seconds. I packed all the clothes I could find, made all the telephone calls I thought were essential, indiscriminately packed one enormous suitcase, and made a rapid tour of the apartment, which already looked uninhabited. The empty medicine cabinet stood open—a silent witness to what had happened to my life. Then it was time to leave.

The cab ride was too short, separating me, in a matter of minutes, from everything and everyone I knew and loved. We drew up before an enormous house—a beautiful, Palladian house—where the taxi disgorged us in front of a huge snow bank. Alan hefted the suitcase over the snowdrifts to the door and I followed slowly, savoring my last free breath of air. My last for twenty-eight days.

Yes, iron gates clanged shut behind me. They actually did! Inside, I glanced around quickly and saw a polished marble floor and sweeping staircase in a room that looked like a movie set. Facing the door sat a receptionist (none too friendly) and in an office to the left were several bustling, busy females (not at all friendly). Alan and I were instructed to sit down and wait. People wandered by and stared at us. I tried not to think. If I thought, I'd come apart. I'd just be too afraid. I wouldn't be able to stay.

Someone called my name and we got up to enter the office.

"You can't go in," they said to Alan. I was going to be all alone with these unfriendly strangers. I clung to Alan for as long as I could, kissed him on the cheek and watched him walk, without looking back, through the doors and out of Smithers. Into the real world and out of my own unreal world. Perhaps forever.

I was alone.

31.

"Sit down, please."

I sat facing a sour-looking blonde who shuffled papers around her desk and turned to address questions to others in the room, ignoring me completely. I sat and said nothing. When, finally, I tried to break the silence, I was hushed with an impatient "Just *wait* a moment, *please*." I knew I didn't like this woman. I felt sure she didn't like me.

She began to fill out a questionnaire.

"When was the last time you took a pill?"

"Ten days ago."

"What pills?"

I listed them all.

"Did you drink?"

"No."

"Are you depressed?"

"Yes."

"What are your symptoms?"

I listed them.

"You're not *clinically* depressed!"

"My shrink says I'm depressed."

"Listen, you're messing up my questionnaire!"

I felt my anger rising. I truly did not like this woman, whoever she was. (She was, I discovered later, the nurse in charge.) We went on and on with the list of questions. I just couldn't answer any of them to her satisfaction.

"You're certainly not the norm."

I felt better.

"You won't fit in at all."

I felt scared again.

When the questionnaire had been completed, the sour-faced nurse turned to me and said, "Open your handbag."

"Why?"

"Just take out all the contents."

I spilled them onto her desk.

"What are those pills?"

"They aren't pills—they're saccharin."

She swooped them into her desk drawer.

"But I need those. I can't have sugar."

"But how do I know they aren't LSD?"

"Try them."

She glared at me furiously.

"Your checkbook, credit cards, and money have to go into the safe. Get a receipt."

They were taken from me, I got my receipt, and was left without funds, without identification and with a sense of total helplessness. I now had no bargaining power at all. I felt naked.

I was dismissed and sent back to the waiting room. The guard—no, he wore no uniform and I discovered later that he, too, was a recovered addict—asked me to open my suitcase and proceeded to go through its contents. This time my cologne was confiscated. "But why?" "You might drink it." Alcoholics, it seems, drink anything that contains alcohol. Even cologne.

I heard a name being called over a loudspeaker and then a girl appeared. She was to be my roommate. One of them, that is. She would escort me to my room. It was two flights up that long and winding staircase. Two flights, dragging that huge suitcase behind me. I staggered onto the second floor, where indolent-looking people were draped over a sofa and chairs in a hallway reception room. The men looked strong enough but made no move toward helping with the suitcase. Finally, we got it up to the next landing and into the room that was to be my new home.

I think back with some amusement on my first view of that room, because my later impression of it was so different. (My visual perception was still screwy. The room looked huge (it was that) and messy and like a place I wouldn't want to spend much time in. I later found it to be warm and tidy and the way everyone would want home to look.

I was shown my bed. Bed? "This is a cot!" Amused expressions around the room. A cot it was. Newcomers always got it, until one of the senior roommates left and the newcomer could graduate to a real bed. "Lots of luck," I was told.

I dumped my suitcase on the floor, where I stumbled over it every time I walked by. I had no lamp, no drawers, no comforts. The closet, at least, was ample, and I began to unpack my things for the month's "visit."

I met my roommates; there were four. Pat, a forty-five-year-old grandmother; Sigrid, a beautiful Swedish model; Becky, a young black welfare mother; and a loud Jewish singer called Mo. The grandmother and the singer were about to be discharged. The young mother was weeping. The model seemed to be sane.

I was close to tears and I had never been more homesick in my life.

It was five o'clock. Dinnertime. I would have my first meal in my new home and begin to learn about Smithers life.

There was a line of hungry patients all the way out the door of the dining room. The dining room was impressive, with French doors that opened onto a terrace, red flocked wallpaper, elaborately carved mantel —all remembrances of other, more affluent times. The dozen or so round tables, stackable chairs, and the mounted swordfish over the mantel were incongruities.

That first dinner was something—one hundred percent starch and sugar. It was an introduction to twenty-eight days of institutional meals, most of which were pretty awful. But before long I, too, would be hungrily standing in line well before dinnertime.

Physically, the Smithers Center is lovely. Housed in the former Billy Rose mansion (a fact they never fail to mention) on East Ninety-third Street in Manhattan, it is precisely the opposite of what one would expect. It is not institutional-looking; it is luxurious. And that helped. Somehow five roommates in an immense, wood-paneled bedroom with a sunny bay window and a fireplace didn't seem quite so bad. So what if one of the beds was *in* the fireplace? There was a sort of black humor to our set-up. There we were, addicts, locked away in our million-dollar suites. There were elaborate bathrooms, built-in scales, and secret compartments. Rumor had it that there was a million dollars sealed into one of the walls. I doubted that Billy Rose could have overlooked this amount of petty cash, but later I would spend a lot of time helping look for secret passages and concealed stashes. It was something to do.

The first evening, like every newcomer, I got a tour of all the rooms. The bathroom in our room was the star of the house, they told me. It was marble, with mirrors everywhere (in which I later saw more than I cared to of my expanded rear end), and a shower so complicated it required a flight check before use. There were dials and more dials, and a huge shower head that could sweep you away. There was a marble tub large enough for (and at times accommodating, they had heard) two. Yep. It all lent a lot of class to a rehab.

I had been given a schedule of daily activities in which I was to participate. I had to keep it before me for a while. Dr. Zuckerman had warned me that going to Smithers was something like going to school. There would be lectures and classes and meetings ad nauseam, and he asked me to try to understand that all of this was vital to my recovery. I was to attend and try to absorb.

There was a lecture scheduled for seven o'clock every night in the week. On my very first night (on *each* Monday night) it was an AA meeting. A simulated AA meeting, to be precise, as we weren't really members of AA. It was meant to acquaint us with the AA methods, for the guidelines of recovery subscribed to by Alcoholics Anonymous were also the guidelines subscribed to by Smithers. We were going to be indoctrinated into the format that would, they hoped, be our way of life in the outside world.

I sat queasily and nervously through it all, feeling utterly helpless when my roommate Becky burst into tears and fled from the room because of some imagined (or real) slight. I had never seen emotions bled all over the place before. In my world, that simply wasn't done.

At eight we were free for the evening. At least everybody else seemed to be free. I heard my name announced on the loudspeaker (the constant prattling of the loudspeaker was a sound we all got used to) and I was summoned to the nurses' station (the desk where I'd answered my entrance questionnaire). It had little to connect it with nursing except for a scale and a blood-pressure machine standing nearby. I was given another going-over by the nurse on duty—a young kid in knee socks and clogs. I weighed in and had my blood pressure taken and my heart checked. The blood-pressure check was a routine thing for the first week, day and night. I later learned it was intended to signal convulsions before they began. Thank God I didn't know that then.

And so I went to my room to deal with my first night at Smithers.

Try to sleep on a folding cot with half the springs missing, multiply the discomfort by four (for four snoring roommates), and you get some idea of how I felt. Sleep? Well, I hadn't slept before, so why should I now? My first night found me up, down, feeling my way to the bathroom in the dark, tiptoeing to avoid the wrath of wakened roommates, finally giving up and creeping downstairs to the lounge, where I had been told I could always find tea and companionship. True. There was always someone awake around Smithers. Addicts notoriously do not sleep. The addict, once withdrawn from the drug of choice, often must wait weeks, sometimes months, before he sleeps normally again. Sedatives (including alcohol) bring on unnatural sleep, while they destroy natural sleep. It takes time—lots of time—before those natural sleep patterns return. But they always do. On that first night, however, despairing of rest, I did not believe that one day I would sleep soundly, peacefully, restfully, and naturally without the help of any chemical.

To kill time, I studied the schedule I had been given on admission. It gave the name of my counselor, Anna (she was, I heard, the ogre of the place), my therapy group (it was, I heard, the best group in the house), my room and bed number (no bed-swapping; we were numbered), and all the activities I was expected to participate in every day. It went like this:

7:00 A.M.	Everybody up
7:30 A.M.	Breakfast
9:00 A.M.	Lecture
10:00 A.M.	Group Therapy
12:00 Noon	Lunch
1:30 P.M.	Lecture
2:30–5:00 P.M.	Free Time
5:00 P.M.	Dinner
7:00 P.M.	Lecture
8:00–11:00 P.M.	Free Time
11:00 P.M.	Lights out

On Saturday there was something called "Big Group," which, my roommates had explained, meant the entire "student body," gathered in a circle in the big lecture room (Billy Rose's salon) for confrontation therapy. It was nobody's favorite activity.

Sunday, from one until five, was visitors' day. I wondered whether I could hold out until then.

32.

My first week in Smithers was an agonizing assault on all my senses. Withdrawal was severe, and the medical watch was still on in case I suffered seizures. I continued to have visual disturbances: rooms were out of proportion, people were out of proportion, and I saw flashing lights where there were none. I saw an extra person in our therapy group one day and later realized it had been my imagination. (A hallucination? I didn't know.) I walked down the spiral staircase holding on to the wall, because the stairs seemed to be rolling beneath my feet. My mental and physical perceptions were confused, and I no longer knew what was real and what was in my head. (I knew that the rotten state of my nerves was very real indeed.)

I was told to report any visual problems to the nurse, and each time I did, the Smithers doctor, Dr. Martin, was summoned to examine me. He always pronounced me a normal withdrawal case, but they kept on watching me carefully all the same.

My sleep did not improve. Most nights I prowled the lounge with the rest of the sleepless patients. I drank milk and slept for another hour or so and then was up again. When Sigrid got up at six I was always relieved. We had early-morning tea together and our day officially began.

The doors at Smithers were always open, we were told—but woe to the patient who tried to use them! They were for the use of visitors and staff only and we could walk out any time, all right, but we sure as hell couldn't get back in. A breath of fresh air from the sidewalks of Ninety-third Street was a simple pleasure that was forbidden for twenty-eight days. Freedom had never seemed so precious to me. Freedom had never been so unavailable.

We were incarcerated within the walls of our mansion, and movement within those walls became our only activity. If you think of a rehab as classes in yoga, or breathing-and-relaxing exercises, forget it. Getting any exercise at all was our problem. The staff would deal with our besotted minds; they didn't give a damn about our bodies. Everyone gained weight on the starch-and-sugar diet. My low-carbohydrate diet had been forgotten in the interest of staying alive. Oddly, the only ill effect seemed to be showing in my shape. Shakes, sweats, headaches, and other hypoglycemic problems stayed away. It blew all the hypoglycemia theories to hell and back. But fat was all I got.

My life had always been a study in perpetual motion, and I resented the confinement of the Smithers life. I developed my own exercise program by running up the spiral stairs—three flights, all the way from the lobby to the top floor. With the baronial ceiling heights at Smithers it was no easy feat, but as the days passed, it got easier and easier until soon I was leaping about like a gazelle, scaling the heights like a mountain goat. I looked, though, like a baby whale.

My stair-running did nothing for my fat. I gained twenty pounds anyway. Everybody gained twenty pounds. It was as if it had been planned, and secretly we blamed the staff for conspiring to stuff us into submission. But we continued to eat, and considering the quality of institutional food, that should tell you a lot about our psyches. Eating was the only recreation we had, and we ate every meal as if it might be our last.

At six-thirty every morning the dining room was bustling with the early-morning-coffee crowd. We always hoped for a real breakfast and were usually disappointed. Breakfast was cold cereal and toast. Now and again we were surprised with eggs and bacon, and when we were surprised two days running we were seduced into believing that a real breakfast would become a daily repast. Not so. Inevitably it reverted to cold cereal and toast. A little more starch to fuel the fire of fat.

By eleven-forty-five we were lined up again, for lunch. Meals wer served cafeteria style, with the lines of the hungry moving past enor mous pots, out of which food was ladled onto our plates. It looked like James Cagney prison flick, except we stopped short of banging ou spoons on our plates. And the plates, at least, were not metal.

The cooks were unfathomable. Some of the food was sublime. Soup were delicious and homemade. Occasionally meals were just plain good other times they were a symphony in white: potatoes, corn, and fish Often they were just plain inedible.

Everyone was ravenous again, anyway, by five o'clock, and we fough for first place in line (the lucky bums who set tables that week were al ready inside). We wheedled our way into the good graces of the cooks hoping for larger servings or choicer tidbits. We took three dessert while we waited for food. (The less wily ended up with none.) At man meals dessert was the only thing fit to eat.

At eight o'clock cold cuts and cheese were brought out from th kitchen and were gone before the platters reached the table. Supposedl civilized adults assaulted the servers like savages. I took a good look a my behavior on one occasion and thereafter gave up cold cuts.

But I continued to eat. Visitors brought cookies and potato chips an fruit. The fruit lay there and rotted while we gorged on the sweets. W sent a friendly porter to buy more goodies, while bankers, stockbrokers surgeons, and street people all tried to trade favors for a chocolate chi cookie. To what had we all been reduced? To children, which is what in a funny way, we were.

When I look back I see that the sugar consumption made up for, in many cases, the withdrawal from a steady supply of false energy in th form of alcohol. Standard supplemental treatment for alcoholism seem to be a substitute supply of sugar. Theoretically, the substitution wil keep you off the booze. It works, too, most of the time, if the alcoholi (recovered alcoholic, that is) is careful to eat the sweet in time—befor the craving for alcohol becomes insupportable. More often than not, boost to the blood sugar is what was needed all along.

I have my own theories about blood sugar and alcoholism, because have never come across an alcoholic—certainly not in my own family— who didn't have either a diabetic or hypoglycemic problem. (The tw are not diseases at opposite ends of the pole, as their names might sug gest. Low blood sugar is very often the forerunner of high blood sugar or diabetes.)

All in all, blood-sugar aberrations, it would seem, have a great dea to do with making a person susceptible to the disease of alcoholism. As yet, no one can say for sure. But *I* believe that if you have a blood-sugar problem, you'd best part company with alcohol. And if you can't have alcohol, you can't have any addictive substance. And, furthermore, you shouldn't even have sugar. Which leaves you with a great big problem that medical science is going to have to sort out. For sugar is the very worst enemy of abnormal blood sugar. It is death to the diabetic and sends the hypoglycemic into a blood-sugar low.

But sugar, in some odd way, also calms quaking nerves, so I ate sugar in Smithers. I got fat, but I survived. For that moment in time, sugar was my support system.

The faces changed every day. New people appeared, seemingly in homogeneous bunches, and others would graduate. Someone was always bidding a tearful farewell to someone else.

My grandmother roommate went, and I inherited her bed. A real honest-to-God Beautyrest, albeit an ancient, lumpy one. I got a reading light into the bargain.

No sooner had I vacated my cot than I was summoned by loudspeaker to the office and introduced to my newest roommate. Now it was my job to show the newcomer around.

Gloria was pale and visibly shaken as she said good-bye to her mother. We were introduced and told that we would have much in common. She, too, was a pillhead.

Gloria was small, blonde, and scared. Her thin, pinched face was chalky white and her eyes looked like mine—popped out of her head. We would cling to each other for a long time.

This time I dragged *her* suitcase up the stairs, installed her in her cot-corner and heard her story.

Gloria had an alcoholic father, a homosexual husband, and a pill problem. She had shrunk from two hundred pounds to one hundred on amphetamines and she was still flying. Her voice never rose above a whisper, but it never stopped, either. Speed kills, and it had almost killed her. She was a telephone operator by day, a disco queen by night, and she averaged three hours of sleep per. To compensate she ran on synthetic energy—the energy she got from amphetamines. The speed kept her going. It also ate her alive. Her hair was thin and falling out, her teeth were crumbling and hideous, and her insides were a mess. She was only thirty-five and she had gotten to Smithers just in time. Gloria

continued to whisper, nonstop, until she had everybody thoroughly unnerved. And she didn't stop then.

When Gloria arrived, the loud Jewish singer left, and we were four
again. Gloria claimed a bed and we all settled down as roommates: one
child-mother, one speed freak, one alcoholic model, and me.

Pecking order was established forthwith. Seniority was important, for
seniority said who could bend the house rules, when and why. Our
room was divided into senior (Sigrid), junior (Becky), sophomore
(me), and freshman (Gloria). (Later it would seem odd to be the
senior.)

For the moment, the pecking order proclaimed peace, probably because Sigrid and Becky were not aggressive sorts. Gloria and I, the
two junkies, did the talking for the entire room, while the other two
kept to themselves and read, or went off to discuss senior-class stuff
with their own groups. At the time, seniors always seemed to be doing
something momentous . . . taking tests, studying, conferring with their
counselors. It seemed terribly important and big-time, and I wondered
whether I would be as informed by the end of my twenty-eight days as
they seemed to be. Would the secret knowledge they seemed to have
ever be mine? How was it they were "getting" everything, while I still
stumbled around just taking notes and doing as I was told? From my
present vantage point I look back at them cynically now. The ones who
seemed the most confident, the ones who had all the answers, the ones
who were eager to go out and face the world—many of those drank and
took drugs and fell again. Why? I don't know for sure, but I do know
that overconfidence is the enemy of sobriety, and those who are sure
they've licked addiction are the ones most likely to get into trouble. It
was the ones who had a healthy fear of what they might do when they
got out who were more likely to follow the suggestions of the Smithers
staff—suggestions that could save their lives.

A serious graduate student who lived down the hall spent most of her
days studying, reading, and rereading all of the AA literature, and having long, philosophic discussions with Sigrid, who was in her therapy
group. She was so eager to get out and get on with her new-found sober
life. Two days after her "graduation" from Smithers, she called each of
us in turn, drunk and raving. Nobody knew what happened to her after
that. I wondered—maybe part of her eagerness to go face the world may
have been simply eagerness to get to a drink.

But I didn't see that then. The seniors seemed like superhumans

ho'd already won the battle against addiction. I didn't know they were
vulnerable.

We four roommates coexisted peacefully for a while. That was our
ood luck, for disagreements between patients had to be solved by the
atients themselves. Only in a complete stalemate would a staff member
ep in to arbitrate. It was one more lesson from Smithers: they'd give
ou all the tools, but they wouldn't fight your battles for you. We were
arning to cope with life.

Sigrid was my favorite roommate, partly because she was so beauti-
ul. It was inconceivable to me that Sigrid had been a sloppy drunk. She
ad everything. She was tall—five-nine in her socks—and one of those
nprobable Scandinavians with coal-black hair and brilliant blue eyes.
orgeous. She must have weighed no more than 112, soaking wet, and
lothes hung on her with the unstudied elegance that is typical of the
ashion model. At least we had fashion in common.

But very little else. Remote and somewhat haughty, Sigrid showed
recious little emotion save for high-pitched telephone tirades against a
ysterious lover, who was, as she put it, "in the rackets." High-profit
ackets, obviously, since beautiful Sigrid was jet-setted to all the best
ars, knew all the Beautiful People, and was supported in high alco-
olic style. After an early, brief marriage to a wealthy socialite whose
wn alcoholism had, finally, cost him his life, Sigrid had settled down
ith an even richer stockbroker, who was, she said, the very model of a
oring man. Not only that. He kept insisting she give up modeling to
ake *him* her career, and they fought bitterly each time the subject
ame up. And so she drank. By the time she got to Smithers, Sigrid was
irting with physical and emotional disaster. She had finally been res-
ued, by her one remaining female friend, from the urine-and-vomit-
oaked bed where she'd lain in a drunken stupor for a week. She was
ipped to a hospital for detoxification and from there to Smithers. She
as still under thirty and still beautiful. And she was still married,
ough her husband rarely called. The lover did—every night.

Becky, the young mother, was an enigma. She was sweet, friendly,
nd pretty. Becky had untapped artistic talents. She also had temper
ntrums and uncontrolled fits of weeping. Her two children—each by a
ifferent father—were farmed out to foster parents, and she spent a
reat part of each day writing letters to them that they would never
ead. She had thrown the younger child out of a second-story window in
n attempt at murder-before-suicide. He survived. Becky did, too, just

barely. A neighbor dropped in to deliver the older child as the bloo
ran out of Becky's wrists into the tub. She was saved.

For what, she did not know. Becky had spent her life on the stree
and her life was devoted to booze and drugs. There was nothing sh
hadn't tried, from pot to heroin. Finally, the people at Welfare name
her an unfit mother and took her children. After another unsuccessf
suicide attempt (this time by poison), she, too, was shipped off to
hospital and from there to Smithers. Welfare would foot all the bill
from Smithers to the children to the halfway house that, hopefully
would see Becky sober through the next six months. She was twenty
lovely, and lovable. And she was infinitely sad.

And there I was, managing to fit in. When I write about my friends a
Smithers, they sound depressing. They were not. It was hard to live wit
them day by day, sharing jokes and experiences and worries an
sadness, without thinking of them only as friends and not as addicts. B
the same token, they were friends to me, though the alcoholics pro
fessed complete horror over my pill habit. We were all, quite simply, i
the same addictive boat. We were like the inhabitants of a college dorr
and we behaved like kids. Weighty responsibilities had, for the moment
been lifted from us.

The "street people" were far and away the most attractive people i
the place—and the most frightening. They were fiercely emotiona
highly excitable, barely articulate, and omnipresent. Those of us wh
knew nothing about life in the streets got close to, and understoo
street people, while those who had never known the luxury of a bed t
themselves took us middle-class patients as friends. We were an od
mixture, one almost impossible to understand, except that we all ha
addiction in common. An addict is an addict is just an addict.

Street people are often just that—people who have no home save th
city streets. People who sleep on park benches and huddle in doorway
and who carry all their belongings in sacks. Or street people can b
those who are wise in the ways of the street. The children of Harlen
Hell's Kitchen, or any neighborhood where the street is preferable t
what is called "home." Children of the ghettos.

The street people at Smithers came in all ages, sizes, colors, and de
grees of addiction. They were black, white, and Hispanic. Men, womer
and near-children. Children of seventeen, street-smart, old beyond thei
years. Unwed mothers, fathers who'd deserted their families, loner

who lived on the Bowery, and children of middle-class families who somewhere went wrong.

The violence that was endemic to the streets occasionally spilled over into Smithers. Violence was never too far beneath the surface and everybody walked gingerly around the street people. You never quite knew when they'd take offense.

When they did it was usually with one of their own. One of the few times during my stay that the Smithers staff had to spring into action was when two women went at each other with broken bottles. Fortunately, I was safe in my room and only heard the uproar. Those who were there retreated in haste, shaken. The next morning, the two adversaries steered clear of each other in the dining hall, and there was no more physical violence between them. A later graduate told me there was a fight almost to the death one day over who should use the shower first. This, too, was settled posthaste by the faculty. Why no one was ever hurt, I'll never know. Somehow the staff always overcame. By intimidation, I would guess.

The blacks stuck to themselves—mostly, in front of the television set, where "Soul Train" and "Dance Party" and cartoons screamed on. Nobody dared suggest that the rest of us would prefer something else. We more or less gave up the television to the blacks, though there were mutterings about cartoons that had racial-slur overtones. The mutterings were always done *sotto voce*.

If the street people were a close-knit crowd, the rest of us were, quite simply, a motley crew. (There was, of course, nothing simple about anyone in the place.) There were schoolteachers and stockbrokers and doctors and lawyers, a nun, a monk, and a priest. There was Catholic, Jew, and Wasp. Addiction, whether to alcohol or pills, is a great leveler, and in the face of it, we were all equal. Equally helpless.

Against all odds we became one big, happy family. That we could be happy at all tells a lot about the indomitability of the human spirit. I know now what brings fragile humans through disasters. The spirit is strong and the will to survive is the strongest will of all. Recovering addicts may be the strongest people of all.

They must be if they can survive long enough to seek help. Addicts die in great numbers. Every day we were told that exactly half of us—the Smithers folk knew from experience—would end up drinking again or taking drugs. And of that half, more than half would die of their addiction. "Death" was a word we were never allowed to forget. Death was what awaited us, should we slip and fall.

33.

The first week I kept expecting to meet my counselor. Everyone else seemed to have regular appointments with theirs, but apparently my counselor wasn't dying to meet me. I had heard about Anna. Whenever I mentioned her name to someone, they groaned. "Oh, my God!" "That bitch!" "Good luck!" Terrific. Leave it to me to get the lemon of the lot. Finally, the start of my second Smithers week, I was summoned to Anna's office. I was as frightened as a third-grader called to the principal's office.

Anna was scary—tall, big, and severe. She was also, thank heaven, kind. Anna was to be my salvation for a long time to come.

Anna had a lot of questions for me to answer and they were not pleasant. They were about my family, Alan, myself. They were about the amount I drank and the pills I took. She noted my answers to every query. Could she write to my family and to Alan? She could. Did I want to see their replies? I did.

There was a lot of talk about my health. Had I ever had a seizure? I mentioned finding myself on the floor that night in November. She questioned me further. How far was I from the bed? Was I bruised? Was I weak? When I finished my description, she said, "You had a convulsion." I felt shaky. I had never even fainted in my life and here was

Anna, telling me I'd had a convulsion! There was no other way I could have bruised myself so badly in a simple fall. I had been there, alone and convulsing. I was alive by one more miracle. Although I'd told my doctor that next morning, he'd never suggested such a thing. But, of course, nobody understood my addiction then.

Anna called me a "garbage head." She might just as well have said, "You're garbage." By then I had a pretty disgusting picture of myself and my addiction and I hated what I saw. But I must be one tough-as-nails dame, Anna figured. I was alive even though I had, apparently, taken enough drugs to kill your average strong man. But the tolerance I'd developed over so many years meant they hadn't been able to kill me—yet. It had only been a matter of time, though, and the seizure was the first real and clear warning that my time was running out. The scariest part of all was I hadn't heard the warning.

I was dismissed from Anna's office with a printed page on which to write an essay on my addiction. It was called, in the inimitable Smithers jargon, the "First Step Prep." It was the form that would enable me to take the first step in the Twelve Steps of Alcoholics Anonymous—the Twelve Steps that are the basis of the AA recovery method.

The First Step of AA is the first step to recovery and requires admitting that you are powerless over alcohol (or drugs) and that your life has become unmanageable. (An addict's life is undeniably unmanageable.)

The first page of the paper was "Examples of Powerlessness."

Be specific. Give at least five examples of each. Who was involved? What happened? More or less when? What chemicals?

And then there were spaces for:

Blackouts
Destructive Behavior
Accidents or Dangerous Situations Created
Preoccupation With Chemical Usage
Attempts to Control Chemicals and/or Behavior
Loss of Control of Chemicals and/or Behavior

The next page asked for:

Examples of Unmanageability: Be specific. Give at least five examples of each with or without the use of alcohol or other mood-altering chemicals:

Family Life
Social Life
Spiritual Life
Business or Work Life
Financial Life
Physical Condition
Sex Life

I swore that most of these things simply didn't apply to me. I was told to take the sheet and work on it until I had come up with five items for each subject. Anna felt sure that once I began to write, plenty of examples would become apparent. I wasn't convinced but I took the paper and went back to my room—to try.

When I began to write, I found that the spaces on those two sheets of paper weren't large enough to hold the examples from my own life. Here they are, as they were written on that day.

Blackouts:

1. 1977, Nov. Found myself on the floor of my dressing room. Had taken my usual dose of 1 Placidyl, 2 Fiorinal, 2 Valium, 1 Navane, and turned to walk to bedroom. Awoke some time later on floor. Do not know how I got there.
2. 1975. After taking heavy dose of painkillers (Percodan, Librax, Fiorinal, Valium, Navane) for pancreas attack received 6 phone calls, of which I remember only 5.
3. During past years have often been told of phone conversations I do not remember. At this point was taking:

Fiorinal
Valium
Placidyl, 3 strengths
phenobarbital
Librax
Percodan
Navane

I do not recall any other blackouts attributable to pills. There were many times when I experienced blackouts due to alcohol. I am here, however, for pill addiction and will limit my answers to instances that apply directly to pills.

Destructive Behavior:

1. Took alcohol on top of barbiturates and other strong medications. Dur-

ing any given day I took large amounts of Fiorinal, Valium, Placidyl, Navane.

2. 1976, Christmas. Was so depressed by what I considered to be a "put down" by my father that I swallowed several of every pill in my collection, hoping I would pass out. Had to be taken to hospital emergency room.
3. 1977, Summer. Had two automobile accidents due to impaired vision. (Both minor, luckily.)

Accidents or Dangerous Situations Created:

1. 1977. Began to use alcohol when tolerance to sleeping pills increased so much as to make them useless. Because I had pancreatitis any alcohol could be fatal.
2. See automobile accident above.
3. See *Blackouts*—just missed hitting head on furniture when I fell.

Preoccupation with Chemical Usage:

1. Always refilled prescriptions in double amount to be sure I did not run out.
2. Carried entire bottle of Valium and one of phenobarbital in purse.
3. Asked for new prescription when down to 30 Valium.
4. Got friend who is dentist to write Valium prescription even though large amount was expected by mail.
5. Asked for (and got) 3 different strengths of Placidyl to satisfy any degree of sleeplessness. Always took more than prescribed dosage.

Attempts to Control Chemicals and/or Behavior:

1. Made no attempts at all, believing that my preoccupation was normal. (In 1972 gave up alcohol completely—recognized alcoholism but transferred dependence to sedatives.)

Loss of Control of Chemicals and/or Behavior:

1. By 1978, doses were enormous.
2. Had vicious arguments with boyfriend, some of which resulted in my hitting him. (I do not go in for physical violence when I am normal.)
3. Could not perform while writing or talking to editors or make radio or TV appearances without Valium.
4. Could not go away even for one night without dragging suitcase full of medication.
5. Arranged to have duplicate "stash" of pills at house of boyfriend in case I wanted to spend night.

And on the next page:

EXAMPLES OF UNMANAGEABILITY:

Family Life:

1. Can find no effect on family. My parents live in the South. However, father and brother concerned with number of pills I took.

Social Life:

1. Became increasingly withdrawn. Cancelled almost every social engagement I made.
2. Became extremely dependent on boyfriend. Refused to make new acquaintances.
3. Often felt too ill to keep engagements, too tired, too depressed.
4. Made no attempt to maintain contact with old friends. Telephone formerly rang constantly; now many friends have given up and stopped calling.

Spiritual Life:

1. Could not pray as specifically and earnestly as did in past.
2. Often was too nervous to sit through church services.
3. (Spiritual life affected less than other aspects.)

Business or Work Life:

1. Became irritated if my work was criticized, was relatively abusive to those wishing to change it.
2. Became lethargic towards taking full-time job, preferred free-lance so I could work when I felt strong enough.
3. Typing and writing skills badly affected by drugs.
4. My work far from my usual standards. Many jobs refused or redone.

Financial Life:

1. Spent average of four hundred dollars per month on prescription medication.
2. Refused to take full-time job, relying on free-lance.
3. Spent enormous amounts on doctors to cure conditions which I later found to be drug side effects.
4. Jobs began to decline. Work not up to par.

Physical Condition:

1. Had acute pancreatitis caused by drinking.
2. Side effects of drugs, loss of vision, loss of muscular control, falls, stomach pains, swollen abdomen, migraine headaches, constipation, rapid loss and gain of weight beyond normal limits.

Sex Life:

1. Diminishing interest in sex.

And that was my "First Step Prep."

Reading it over, as I do now, makes me shudder, for it brings back ever so vividly the horror of my life as it was then. The filled-out form was a word picture of a life in ruins, courtesy of addiction. It was my job then to put that life back in order.

34.

The rhythm of our days was predictable and steady—meals alternating with lectures and therapy. The music was the same, but the words changed every week. During their third week, patients were assigned "therapeutic duties." Sigrid told me that therapeutic duties did not mean housecleaning or dishwashing, as I had feared—there was staff for that. (I was not to be Cinderella amid the ashes.) It meant that during your entire third week, you got to set tables for every meal. She said it was a mixed blessing. It was a pain in the ass to have to be up at six o'clock but the earlier you hit the kitchen, the better your chances of making small talk with the chef, thereby making off with all the choice stuff. Formidable as they sounded, our "therapeutic duties" were only an exercise in getting to a certain place at a certain time every day for a week. In other words, taking responsibility. Some took it willingly and others bribed friends to take it for them. Addicts!

Bed-making was the only real household chore we had. We were expected to have beds made before breakfast and we stripped them for new linens once a week. With the bed linens came one clean towel, and it didn't take long for everyone to discover that one towel a week wouldn't make it. Most of us called on friends to bring fresh supplies. I had never known towels could be so important.

It was surprisingly easy, however, to get little chores attended to. Every day we wrote out lists of things we needed from "outside." We put the list and some cash in an envelope, and back came the items with all the change, accomplished by the virtuoso performance of our porter, a man whose unfailing good humor cheered us when we were down. It was the first time in my adult life that I'd had someone to do my errands. Naturally, most of the cash went for cookies and potato chips, but we got our cleaning attended to and we were able to have our favorite brands of soap, toothpaste, and tissues—things one never thinks about until they're not there.

Being without money was strange, but money wasn't part of our economic setup. We checked out of the safe (five dollars at a time) what we needed for frivolities like cookies. In the entire twenty-eight days, I think I spent twelve dollars. (Thrifty, but not a form of budgeting I'd recommend.) For an inveterate shopper like me, it was frustrating, because, though we got the newspapers with all their tempting ads, I couldn't phone-order a thing. All my credit cards were locked up in that safe, along with my checkbook. My spring wardrobe would have to wait.

Every morning at nine, breakfast taken care of and beds made, we all took our seats in the lecture hall—that paneled drawing room of Billy's —and settled down for the first lecture of the day. Generally it was delivered by the director of Smithers, Bob de Vere. De Vere was small, solid, tough, and completely charismatic. I couldn't tell his age (fifty? sixty?) for he seemed ageless. I didn't know his background (professor? frustrated actor?), and it didn't matter. Bob de Vere could cope with any alcoholic on earth. Could and did. Every lecture was a lesson in dramatic effect, and every lecture had its desired effect on us. The desired effect was to impress upon us the deadly dangers of alcoholism. (Those patients who took only pills were told to substitute mentally the word *pill* or *chemical* for *alcohol*. I, of course, could use the words interchangeably.)

Bob de Vere never let us forget what we were and where we came from. His lectures were laced with horror stories about those who had forgotten and had ended up dead, and every day the number grew larger. When de Vere appeared with a solemn face and said nothing, we knew that either someone out there had died or de Vere had discovered a bottle. Empty liquor bottles appeared, inexplicably, from time to time on the premises of Smithers. De Vere would bring each one to lecture and hold it up, pause for effect, and launch into all the horror stories he knew about alcoholics who sobered up, drank again, and died.

De Vere rarely fraternized with the patients, which made him seem all the more mysterious. Anyone called to his office (he saw everyone individually at least once before graduation) usually emerged somewhat rattled. Bob had a way of calling you on everything you said. If you started a sentence with "I think . . . ," de Vere always snapped, "With what?" In his view, we were incapable of rational thought and had proved so beyond doubt. Why else would we be in Smithers? Now it was our job to listen to those who knew how to think for us. De Vere was revered by most of us, despised by some, held in awe by everyone.

When I think about the Smithers staff, it is with deepest admiration and affection. (After all, they saved my life.) The Smithers staff knows its job to the letter. The staff is made up largely of recovered alcoholics. That is why they can read the alcoholic patient's mind before it's worked its way through the alcohol fog to an idea. They know every trick in the book and they cannot be deceived. They are fond of saying, "You can't bullshit a bullshitter." And you can't. We all tried.

The Smithers treatment is direct. Beat the patient to his knees (figuratively, of course) and then teach him to obey. In the case of an addict, it is the only way to save his life. In Smithers our every defense was removed. Later those defenses would be rebuilt, but for now we were utterly naked. We were at the mercy of the Smithers staff.

And they were merciless and relentless. They never let us forget about alcohol, they never let us forget our misuse and abuse of alcohol (and/or drugs), they never let us forget that it was alcohol combined with our own stupidity that got us to Smithers. If "stupid" was a word that offended us, that was too bad. Stupid was what we were.

The attitude of the staff was that we had abdicated our rights when we got ourselves in enough trouble to get us into Smithers. They didn't give a fig for our "rights."

Addicts are self-destructive. Addicts will use any devious means to obtain the drug of choice. Addicts will use any excuse for their own addiction. Addicts refuse to admit their addiction. Addicts lie. Addicts cheat. Addicts are sick.

If we got sick of hearing all of this, then we heard it some more. We heard plenty about addiction.

Professionals know that addiction is not weakness of character. Addiction is a potentially fatal disease. The American Medical Association, several years back, officially designated alcoholism a disease—one that can be arrested, but never cured. The addict/alcoholic who believes he is cured is staring death in the eye. And so in Smithers, we were brainwashed: You are sick, you are sick, you are sick. You are incapable of making judgments, you are incapable of thinking, you are incapable of taking care of yourself, you are incapable. We, the staff, are capable. You, the patients, are not. Do as we say and you will be well. Don't do as we say and you will surely die. The word "death" was used a lot. Death is a real possibility for the addict. Death or worse. Worse is the living death, the death of the madhouse, the death of the loss of mental control, the loss of physical control, the "wet brain," the vegetable. We were told to hope for real death should we slip into our addiction again. Death by addiction was the adversary we would face every day for the rest of our lives. Smithers would try to tip the odds in our favor.

At ten o'clock every morning, we adjourned to different rooms for our group therapy. (My group, by chance, met in my room, which somehow made it less scary.) At Smithers, group didn't mean support; group meant confrontation. Usually I sat with my arms wrapped around me in a totally Freudian protective posture and prayed no one would pick on me that day. If I made myself small enough, perhaps I would go unnoticed and therefore unconfronted. It worked most of the time.

The group was always in flux, as patients came and went. At one time it consisted of a garrulous schoolteacher, who came across as Miss Priss when sober, but apparently had been anything but, when drunk, which had been always; an executive of an oil company, who had been pulled in from Saudi Arabia with a get-off-the-sauce warning from his company and come-home-or-else warnings from his wife; a shy, soft-spoken boy who'd just done six years for assaulting his brother; a practically non-English-speaking, noncommunicative enigma of a man, who may have been brain-damaged; a surgeon who shot dope; a young, black, woman executive whose company was footing her sobering-up bill; a flamboyant Lesbian, partially paralyzed on one side; a writer suffering from writer's block and a mama complex; Carl, a steelworker who had fallen from a rigging and spent a year in a cast, drunk; Joey, an amateur prize-fighter who'd killed a man in a fight out of the ring; and me.

Our group leader, Mel, was small, quiet, big-eyed, and black. He was

one of the most competent therapists I've ever come across. And M
was tough.

Not tough as in mean. Tough as in knowing the score. Tough as
being able to cope with alcoholics. And Mel's tough meant taking wh
we handed out and giving it back with interest. Tough meant v
couldn't bullshit Mel.

Group was a new experience for most of us. I was terrified by tl
idea of any confrontation at all, fearing that I wouldn't be able to stan
the terrible things they'd say to me. Things I'd heard them say to other
"You're full of shit," Mel told the quiet young boy. "All you want t
do is drink, you don't want to do a thing about your life, and you'
blaming it all on your brother. It's you, man, and nobody else that
your problem." While the boy looked at the floor and wept.

There were tears and long silences and always fights. Not fistfights
Smithers wouldn't tolerate those—but fierce verbal ones. "You mothe
fucking son-of-a-bitch," shouted the prize-fighter to Carl. "I hate you
motherfucking guts and I'm just gonna hang you on the wall over the
if you don't *shut up* and get off my back, you motherfucker, you leav
my wife out of this, and I'm gonna kill you, too, Mel, you black son-o
a-bitch!" I was prepared to dive under the bed if the need arose.
didn't. Mel, in his quiet voice, promised to expel both Joey and Car
who was protesting, "I didn't say a goddamned word!" But nobody wa
beaten up and nobody was expelled. Everybody, however, was shaken

Most of the time, though, nobody confronted me. Except about Ala
"He's a fuckin' alcoholic! You just want to be with him so you ca
drink! Get rid of him! You're gonna get drunk if you don't."

"I'm not and I won't," was all I could say. Though I wondere
whether they were right about Alan.

The writer went home to deal with his writer's block and his mam
At least we wouldn't have to listen to the telephone harangues betwee
the two, which would have been ludicrous had they not been so p
thetic. "Mama, I told you to leave me alone!" whined the fifty-six-yea
old man into the phone. It was typical of the sort of situation that ha
driven many to drink. What Smithers hoped to do was change the wa
we *dealt* with such situations and relationships.

We were soon joined in our group by the resident loudmouth,
salesman who reveled in his alcoholism and drew enemies the way suga
gets flies. He was the thorn in our side for twenty days, and everybod
loathed him. Just once, I felt sympathy for this repulsive man and ten

porarily forgave him his obnoxious ways. Given an inch of friendliness, he gave out with a mile of louder and more infuriating blather. We all retreated from him and left him to go on alienating himself. Unfortunately, he never left us in peace.

I was sure my group had all of the weirdos in the place. Almost all. Gloria, it seemed, was being the weirdo of her group, her hyperfrenetic manner driving everyone mad. As I listened to her, day and night, in the room, I thanked God for giving me one hour of relief from Gloria's nonstop whisper.

None of my roommates, in fact, shared my group. I liked to believe it was planned that way.

35.

To my amazement, by the second week I had slept through one of the night prowls of the flashlight-bearing nurse. I hadn't slept much, but I had slept soundly. It was a beginning.

In the second week, our fifth roommate arrived. She was big, she was rough and she was tough. She was going to occupy the cot until Sigrid left. Her name was Mary. Mary is a grand old name, but Mary wasn't a grand old girl. Mary had done time. She'd been found one day, passed out next to the body of her lover. Her switchblade knife was in his head. Mary told me she didn't know how it had gotten there, but she went to jail anyway.

Mary had seven kids; they lived with her mother. When she got out of jail, she too went home to mother, who continued to care for the kids while Mary hit the streets. She mainlined heroin, switched to legal methadone, and finally freaked out on cheap wine and Sterno. When she did, her mother saw to it that Welfare got her into a hospital and then into Smithers. Mary was a Welfare freeloader, and she made it clear that Smithers was her winter vacation. Her latest man was waiting to take her back to the bars as soon as she got out. She didn't really

ave a booze problem, she said. This was the first time she'd had a
oom with just four other people in it.

Mary made friends on another floor and never associated with us—for
which we gave fervent thanks.

And so our number, and our pecking order, was complete. We settled
own to count the days and wait for graduation.

There were daily dramas in my group. The young oil executive was
osing his wife, who was losing patience with his ongoing hospi-
alization. He not only had to deal with being withdrawn from alcohol,
e had to deal with the disintegration of his marriage.

All of us seemed to be fearful of losing our husbands, wives, lovers.
All of us had good reason. Alan telephoned every day, but I thought he
ounded remote. I fantasized about the women he had while he was not
aving me. For all I knew, Alan had given up on me. There was hardly
person in the group who didn't have similar doubts.

The shy young boy who'd almost murdered his brother was a prob-
em. He did not believe he was an alcoholic. He refused to say he was
n alcoholic. He simply had hated his brother. But he wasn't an alco-
olic, he insisted. Because of that we were treated to our first psycho-
rama. The lights were doused and we were all silent. Mel (incredibly
nd almost visually) became the boy's dead mother. "I am your
other. Is there anything you want to say to me?" Long silence. Fi-
ally, "I love you." "I love you, too. Are you all right?" "Why did you
ave to leave me? Couldn't you have stayed?" "No. I had to go."
Why? Why did you leave me? You knew I loved you." "I had to go."
I'm so sorry. I loved you so much. But why were you always drunk?"
y now the boy was sobbing uncontrollably, Mel's face was drawn and
is chin trembled, and I felt tears running down my cheeks. There were
uffled noises around the dimly lit room and I realized that the oil ex-
cutive, who stood at my side, was weeping. All of the boy's pain came
oilling out . . . his drunken mother had deserted him by dying. He had
epaid her by becoming a drunk himself and by almost killing the
rother he believed to have been her favorite child. He sobbed and
obbed some more, and group was over and we all filed out in silence.
We'd had a look into a human soul. It should have broken through the
oy's denial barriers. It did not. He steadfastly refused to admit he was
n alcoholic, and ten days after his admittance to Smithers he received a
therapeutic discharge." It meant they didn't believe they could get
nrough to him. It was Mel's first such action, though not by any means

the first such action taken at Smithers. Mel was not quite himself for [a] few days after that.

The physical scars of addiction were highly visible in Smithers—mo[st] visible, oddly, in the medical contingent. A nurse-patient walked with [a] cane and spent an hour or so at the nurses' station changing the band[age] age on her festering leg wound—the wound that resulted from a co[l] lapsed vein where she'd injected a needle one time too many. Th[e] wound was to be a long time healing. Meanwhile, the surgeon in [our] group argued daily with us about whether or not he was *responsible* f[or] his own addiction.

"How can I be responsible?" asked the surgeon. "I'm addicted. [I] can't help it." "Fuck you!" screamed Carl, the steelworker. "You're [a] fucking doctor! You're supposed to know better!"

The lesbian got on everyone's nerves. She was aggressively and ob[-] noxiously tough, and soon was dubbed "Ruby Begonia" by the e[x] fighter, who loved to tease her. If there was one thing she didn't want, [it] was a feminine nickname. (For on the outside, she was known [as] "Ty"!) Ruby prattled on incessantly about her operations. She sa[id] she'd had thirty-two of them and still her left arm and her left leg we[re] crippled. This meant she had to be babied and fed and bathed. No on[e] relished the idea, but someone always had to do it. (I wondere[d] silently why Smithers had taken in someone so helpless.)

According to Ruby Begonia, fate was against her, and every time sh[e] got up from one operation, life brought her down for one more coun[t]. Finally, the fighter lost his sense of humor and roared, "You damne[d] dyke! You tried to kill yourself, didn't you?" Which is precisely wha[t] Ruby Begonia had done. For Ruby Begonia not only drank, she too[k] Valium, too, and in a moment of guilt and repentance over her who[le] condition in life she swallowed an entire bottle of the little yellow pill[s]. She didn't die, but by the time she was brought to a hospital she ha[d] lain on her left side so long that she had done irreparable nerve dam[-] age. Operations or no operations, Ruby Begonia would never be nor[-] mal again.

And so our therapy group went, day after day for twenty-eight day[s]. Oddly enough, it became everybody's favorite hour of those days.

36.

The worst day of the week was Sunday—visitors' day. Tension began to build on Friday; the staff knew to expect it. (We never learned.) Tempers were frayed and voices were shrill and plenty of words were crossed, all because we were about to be reunited with our families, friends, and lovers. And because the time would be so short.

Visiting hours were strictly enforced, and family and friends who came to Smithers during the week, for family counseling or to bring mail and emergency supplies, were kept far away from us. We were never allowed so much as a glimpse of visitors during the week. But on Sunday afternoons, from one to five, anyone could come.

Every room was filled with one to six visitors per patient, meaning thirty people or so to a room. Forget privacy. Everybody had a little circle of visitors around his or her bed. Our reception rooms were jammed, and everybody met everybody and we all regaled our visitors with the week's gossip, which they probably couldn't have cared less about. Visitors were treated to the mediocre coffee in the dining room and shown about the mansion. Billy Rose's bathrooms were the most impressive things on the tour (ours, of course, was the star) and visitors always weighed themselves on those built-in scales and tried to open the wall safes. Everybody seemed impressed with the *luxe* that was Smithers.

As visitors arrived, patients' names were announced on the loud-speaker and there was much dashing up and down the spiral staircase. (The elevator was always full, and worked sporadically at best.)

If Sunday was sunny, we sat on the terrace wrapped in our coats. Otherwise, we stuck to the crowded bedrooms and public rooms. Then, at five, there was a loudspeaker announcement that visiting hours were over and guests must go. And then tears were shed, and farewells were said, and faces were long.

We all dragged back up the staircase and sank into a collective depression that lasted through Monday. That sinking-stomach feeling—the Sunday night kind—is one I can feel today. Especially as I write about Sunday nights at Smithers.

Sunday night found everybody in his own depressing little world. The staff knew we weren't up to much just then and so we were shown movies on alcoholism. We were expected to write little essays about how the movies made us feel. All of us always felt simply awful.

For once we didn't feel like eating, which was just as well, since Sunday night supper was traditionally the worst meal of the week. (Perhaps the kitchen knew how we felt and pinched pennies that night.)

After we had gloomed through the movie we fought over which TV shows to watch and invariably, during my tenure, ended up watching a rerun of a sci-fi show, for the simple reason that it was the favorite of the biggest, toughest, meanest patient in the place. And nobody felt like fighting on Sunday night. No one talked much and everybody made plans to leave Smithers on Monday morning. But nobody ever did.

Sundays were especially bad for me because I knew Alan and I were growing apart. We hadn't much to talk about. He couldn't take part in any conversation about the events in my day and he would not report any part of his day to me. Alan was always the very last visitor to arrive on Sunday, and I felt sure he was trying to spend as little time with me as possible. There was a distance between us, always, and of course there was never any privacy. I felt nervous with Alan now, but he sat and made small talk with the crowds in our room even when he chose not to chat with me. When Alan and I hadn't much to say, we did the crossword puzzles, though usually I felt too on edge to work at it for very long. Then suddenly visiting hours were over. I always went with

Alan to the door, gave him a peck on the cheek, a long hug, and then watched as he disappeared.

Within half an hour, I was on the phone to Alan. Usually, he didn't answer. Where he spent his time I did not know.

37.

Smithers could enforce the no-fraternizing-between-the-sexes rule all they wanted, but they really couldn't do a thing about "boy meets girl on Smithers campus." I met my boy.

One morning in lecture, a handsome young man slipped into the seat next to mine, draped his arm across my shoulder, grinned, and said, "Hi, who are you?" Who, me? But I was hooked. Enchanted. Charmed. For one thing Gus had plenty of was charm—a fact most of the Smithers females had spotted the moment he'd arrived, just an hour before.

Gus was blue-eyed, curly-haired, and beautiful. He was also exactly half my age. But that didn't seem to matter to Gus. From the moment we met ("Who, me? I'm . . .") we were inseparable.

Gus had come to Smithers from a jail stint (jail terms seemed almost *de rigueur* in Smithers, like some strange badge of honor) for assault with a deadly weapon. I never quite understood what it was all about. Some sort of drunken, doped-up brawl. But even jail hadn't broken Gus's bad booze-and-drugs habits. It had sort of helped them along, in fact. And so Gus's family (which included a beautiful pregnant wife) had deposited him at Smithers as a kind of last-gasp effort before they all gave up on his case.

Gus became my protector and that badge of honor kept all would-be hecklers at his strong arm's length.

The fact that I was old enough to be his mother didn't bother Gus at all. He dug me. He lusted after the woman. He loved the mother image. He admired the mature (*he* thought) mind. And I, though my conscience protested a bit, adored Gus. He made me feel female again. Oh, I knew it was all a little game. But this boy found me attractive! Thank the Lord! For until I met Gus, I hadn't realized the sterility of my relationship with Alan. Had my unrecognized love affair with drugs destroyed my real love affair with Alan? I just didn't know. But Alan didn't seem to want me anymore. And, by God, Gus did. And so I romanticized Gus, jail stint and all. My values were, just then, pretty mixed up.

Roommates tended to hang out together. Sigrid became my closest female friend, and I wanted to hold back the moment when she would leave me. I felt that I would be afloat in a hostile sea without Sigrid. She was the stabilizer of our little abode. Sigrid never lost her Nordic cool (except when her lover didn't call—then "Watch out!"). She did, however, lose her cold-and-haughty posture with me and we relaxed into girl talk and gossip. Sigrid opened up to me about her sexless, pseudo-successful marriage, her sex-filled pseudo-loving affair, and her fears about her future. Sigrid needed success, admiration, a reason for living. Playing the little homemaker had never been part of Sigrid's plans. She'd known fame and she would never adjust to anonymity. Sigrid couldn't face the idea of seclusion in Westchester and she would *never* tolerate the ennui of playing housewife for the stockbroker and playing cards with the other housewives. And so she acquired a lover. When she couldn't face either husband or lover, Sigrid had booze.

Sigrid was the only one who could keep Gloria quiet. Not even Gloria argued with Sigrid when she said, "Shut up." Sigrid and I banded together in efforts to keep Gloria's nonstop talk out of our lives, to keep Big Mary out of our way, and to comfort Becky whenever she wept. We were the senior citizens of the third floor south. But Sigrid would be leaving ten whole days ahead of me, and I wondered how I'd manage without her.

Gloria was a constant problem, still flying on whatever remained of the amphetamines that had filled her system for the past twelve years.

She had used amphetamines the way other people use vitamins, taking as many as thirty a day. Luckily for Gloria her husband had connections, but at a dollar or more a pill, her habit kept them broke.

Gloria was also an emotional mess. She hated her father, who telephoned her when he was drunk, invariably precipitating one of her colitis attacks. (For which she got no medicine at Smithers.) She worried about whether her husband was seeing other women (I translated her worry to "other men") during her confinement. Gloria had plenty of problems, and her problems were our problems, for she never ceased telling us about them. I couldn't help liking Gloria—she was a kindhearted sort—but her nerves rubbed my nerves raw. Although we had our pill problem in common, I tried to keep a distance between Gloria and me.

Becky was never around which was too bad, because when she was not weeping, Becky had a sunny, cheerful, calm disposition and usually made us all feel better. But Becky keenly felt her poverty, even in Smithers. She had too much pride to ask her roommates to lend her soap and deodorant and cigarettes. Nobody minded, for we all loved Becky. But Becky minded a lot.

So she hung out with the Welfare crowd—or at least with the black Welfare crowd. But she was a misfit even there, for Becky had talent, she was chic, she loved beautiful clothes and beautiful things and spent much of her time doing needlework and drawing. She was clever and stylish and good looking, and being just another Welfare case was harder on Becky than it might have been on somebody else. When she felt the injustice of her situation, Becky wept. She would fling herself on the bed, sobbing as if her heart would break, while our hearts broke for her. What could anyone do? She wept for the children she could not have with her, she wept for her life that had been saved—for what?

Big Mary's man came to get her one day. He'd gotten tired of doing the bars all alone. And so Mary walked out, without warning to us and with, we assumed, no permission from Smithers.

That same day we'd acquired another roommate. Another street person. Maxine. Maxine was nobody's friend. Maxine was mean, sullen, silent, and brooding. She was seldom around, which was fine with the rest of us. When she was around, we all steered clear of her. Maxine was a slob. She had no consideration. She hogged the bathroom and left rings in the tub and hair in the basin. And Maxine yelled in her sleep. What nightmares she had, God and Maxine alone knew, but we all lost an awful lot of sleep and became irritable. And that meant trouble.

In a pressure cooker like Smithers, emotions are always on high heat, tempers are in turmoil, and "control" is a word nobody knows. And so the inevitable happened, and it happened when everyone was tense—on a Sunday night.

Lights were out at 11:30. The snores began, and I stuck cotton in my ears. Some time later there was a loud yell and we all leaped from our beds. All except Maxine. She kept screaming in her sleep.

Sigrid lost her temper, and her shouts awakened Maxine, along with most of the rest of the floor. Sigrid was screaming at Maxine that she was sick and tired of being awakened every night and Maxine was screaming back at Sigrid that she had a nerve to wake her up like that. Gloria and I cowered in a corner, and Becky pulled the blanket over her head. Before any of us knew what had happened, Maxine was out of bed and across the floor into the bathroom. There was a crash, and Maxine reappeared with a jagged, broken shampoo bottle in her hand. I didn't believe what I saw. It was a rerun from every penitentiary movie I'd ever seen, but Maxine was real and going for Sigrid, who had turned pale and silent. Except for Maxine's profane shouts—"You white bitch motherfucker, you leave me alone or I'll kill you"—not one of us could utter a word. And then I remembered the sharp hairdresser's shears in the drawer beside my bed. I grabbed for them, and heard myself say in a perfectly calm, flat voice, "You're not going to hurt her or anybody." The door flew open and a nurse and a guard dashed in. Maxine dropped the bottle, and she and Sigrid were hustled downstairs to the nurses' station. Gloria was shaking, Becky wept, and I looked down at the weapon in my hand. There was no doubt at all that I would have used it if I'd had to.

An hour or so later, Sigrid and Maxine returned and got into their beds without a word to any of us. Maxine was silent for the rest of the night. Somebody must have slept, because I heard somebody's snoring. Nothing was ever said about the incident. Nobody wanted to broach the explosive subject.

38.

Something about incarceration brings out the child in everyone. We had cliques and crowds and pet hates and favorite people. We banded together in loathing the loud salesman, and we banded together in loving the soft, shy boy who was being "therapeutically dismissed." We tormented those we disliked and fawned over those who were "approved." We were obnoxious one and all, exactly like grade-school children.

We shared one another's tears and tragedies. Welfare mothers wept over lost babies. (An alcoholic is an "unfit" mother.) Strong men wept over broken marriages. We all worried over lost jobs, lost homes, lost lives.

Lost lives were never far from our minds. At least once a week Bob de Vere would announce that another Smithers ex-patient had been found dead. The age might be thirty-one, twenty-four, or fifty-five. Then he would tote up the number lost thus far. It was impressive. Fifty percent of us would risk losing our lives to drink. It was more than just a chance. It was a statistic. Lost lives were what we could expect if we were to leave Smithers now.

Some people did leave Smithers almost as soon as they'd come. I wondered why they'd come in the first place. One glamorous politico's wife swept in from her limousine, tossed off her mink coat and demanded that it be put in the Smithers safe. The Smithers safe was barely big enough to hold all our wallets, much less mink coats, and so political bride was stuck holding her fur. She fumed and fussed for exactly eight hours, at the end of which she made a furtive phone call to her hubby and checked out, saying that her husband missed her and was sending for her immediately. She telephoned later that night to tell about the wonderful dinner-with-wine she'd had as a marital reunion and she sent her love and farewell to Smithers. For us it was just one more giggle at the end of a long day.

On St. Patrick's Day, we lost one of our neediest cases, a boy of nineteen who had lived out of a midtown telephone booth. Just watching the parade on our sepia television set (the color had been "out" for weeks) made him so thirsty that he gathered up the overcoat that was his only possession and split for Eighty-sixth Street. There he caught the end of the parade, a cold, and a relapse into alcoholism, all at once. We found out all this when he tried to get back into his warm Smithers bed. He was not readmitted, and his chances for survival were not very good.

The rest of us plodded through, one day at a time. Gus and I did laundry together, gaining a bit of privacy in the basement. Sigrid and Gloria acquired a violent dislike for each other. While Sigrid grew cooler, Gloria grew more hysterical. She might have been quiet once but she was getting ornery, and her language was turning blue, even for Smithers. When even the street people began to comment on it, I knew we were seeing a personality change in Gloria. She was no longer shy and frightened. She was getting louder. And she still seemed to be flying. Becky wept all day long. Thank God Maxine stayed away.

We split up into cliques of cardplayers and non-cardplayers, crossword-puzzle fans and readers, TV watchers and disco dancers. Dancing was not a planned activity, but on Saturday morning "Soul Train" always brought out the rhythm in somebody. And there was one-upmanship all the time.

The crossword-puzzle people got up early in order to grab one of the two copies of the *New York Times*. I hated the early bird who always tore out the puzzle and left a hole on the other side. (On Sundays, thank goodness, Alan brought my very own, highly valued copy.)

Other people sat for hours and gossiped in the rotunda outside Billy Rose's salon. There were those who read in the library (quite a misnomer, since the library contained no books) and those who hung out in the dining hall and those who slept all day.

I don't know whether the hilarity around Smithers was from high spirits or hysteria. Take the day that "Priscilla Pocketbook," famous author, reeled out of his Rolls-Royce and into our conclave, dead drunk. (No, you weren't supposed to be drunk when you arrived at Smithers, but many were.) Priscilla was tall, blond, and, as he would be quick to tell you, beautiful. His name was Howard, but his Gucci handbags got him his nickname. Priscilla didn't walk—he slunk. Priscilla arrived late one afternoon, called for a bellboy, was furious at not finding one, bitched about his basement room, ranted about privacy, and inquired as to whether he should dress for dinner. (Nobody knew what "dress" meant to Priscilla.) He arrived for dinner in full disco gear: a gold crocheted jumpsuit over a mini-bikini, a matching Juliet cap on his carefully styled hair. For the first time since I'd been there, the dining hall was silent. When the shock wore off enough for the nurses to regain their composure, Priscilla was led gently but firmly to his room and told that dinner was never *that* formal.

To everyone's surprise, Priscilla turned out to be relatively normal. He was the loving father of a beautiful baby boy, and every Sunday we were treated to the sight of Priscilla and his son—Madonna with child. Soon Priscilla melted into the madness that was Smithers and became just another one of the guys. We were *all* nuts, I think, and when I look back on it now, Smithers seems like one enormous madhouse. But I don't think we realized then just how sick we really were.

Carl, the steelworker, was the class clown. Before his alcoholism he'd been a minor-league stand-up comic, and his hilarious performances helped see us through those sober Sunday nights. Carl did perfect imitations of everyone in the place, including me. Some of them, I suppose, would have been deemed cruel in any other time and place. To us, they were wildly funny. Carl could do a letter-perfect rendition of Priscilla Pocketbook's slinking walk, could perfectly imitate Gloria's nonstop, whispery voice, and Sigrid's Swedish lingo. He aped Ruby Begonia in an exact and thoroughly awful way. We thought it a scream and we collapsed in hysterics at each and every impersonation.

In fact, we collapsed into hysterics often, and I wonder, to this day, whether things were really that funny or whether we were laughing to keep from crying. Well, it was tragi-comedy. Carl did a splendid rendition of the poor unfortunate man on the third floor who had lost his voice box to cancer. Recently, we guessed, for he didn't even have one of those little gadgets that can be held next to the throat to simulate speech. This poor man had to communicate by clacks that emanated from the hole in his throat—a hole that was blessedly concealed from view by a handkerchief tied around his neck. He sounded something like a dolphin, and Carl imitated him perfectly.

One day Carl answered our pay phone, and a female caller asked to speak to our voiceless patient. Carl blurted out, "You can't speak to him—he can't talk!" To which the caller replied, "You're crazy. We have beautiful conversations." The clacker appeared, took the phone, and proceeded to clack away into the receiver. For once, Carl was speechless.

We had plenty of wags and would-be wits about the place. One kept replacing the pigeon's egg in our window-ledge nest with a hen's egg. There were always inmates gullible enough to think the pigeon had laid it!

A lot of laughter was at somebody's expense. I don't think we intended to be cruel, but we roared about the Forty-second Street cowboy, who, when drunk, had spit his false teeth into the toilet and lost them forever. He wandered about Smithers gumming his food and watching the mails for replacement choppers. We chuckled about the brain-damaged boy who built pyramids of cereal boxes in his room. On his departure, the staff discovered two hundred cereal boxes and just as many cans of orange juice. Bits of gallows humor like that kept us amused and kept the camaraderie going.

39.

It took centuries for the medical profession to recognize the disease of alcoholism. Even now there are those who will argue that it is simply a weakness of character. But in Smithers it was drummed into our brains, day and night, that we were sick, sick, sick! The disease, they told us, is a three-fold one of body, mind, and spirit. It attacks indiscriminately. Young and old, male and female, black and white and every other color, homo- and heterosexual, Wasp, Jew and Catholic, educated and ignorant. No one should consider himself safe from alcoholism.

In Smithers they taught us that we were not bad people trying to become good. We were sick people trying to get well. In retrospect, I wish more people could hear that message, for while alcoholics are never completely blameless, they cannot be blamed for having a disease any more than can cancer victims. (What they *can* be blamed for, however, is refusal to seek help.)

We learned that there is no such thing as an "alcoholic personality." We learned that for every "crazy" among us alcoholics there was an equivalent "crazy" among nonalcoholics. Alcoholics, we were told could be as schizophrenic as nonalcoholics or as neurotic or as tubercular or as hypertense. In other words, alcoholics are simply a cross section of society, with all its attendant diseases, and are usually undetectable as alcoholics unless, of course, they are still drinking.

So we were just normal people who happened to have the disease of alcoholism. But we learned that there is some predictability with alcoholism and we learned where it strikes. For example, children of alcoholics stand a fifty-percent chance of becoming alcoholics themselves. (And fifty percent is pretty chancy.) But, at the same time, the genetic factors that transmit alcoholism may skip a generation and land on the grandchildren instead. Alcoholism in the family makes the chances of alcoholism greater. From that there's no escape.

And while there is no alcoholic personality per se, in spite of all the movieland stereotypes, alcoholics do, it seems, have more of certain personality traits, such as impatience, intolerance, and individuality, which, when applied to the alcoholic, translate as "grandiosity." And, for the alcoholic, grandiose pride can be deadly. It can lead one to believe that one can conquer alcohol. No alcoholic ever can.

Studies of alcoholism in twins prove a hereditary predisposition to it. But while alcoholism seems to run in families, it also runs in professions as unrelated as law and carpentry. So who knows whether it's heredity or environment? (As the child of an alcoholic lawyer, I took special note of all these facts.)

At this stage of the medicine game, there's a lot of guesswork involved in what makes an alcoholic. And the game of statistics can come up with some strange answers. If you want to know whether there's a likelihood of your ever becoming an alcoholic, here's the way the numbers shape up:

If you (1) are a man (2) are second-generation Irish (3) have an American Indian ancestor (4) have a lot of education (5) have very little education (6) are a city dweller (7) have a comfortable income (8) are married to someone outside your own faith (9) are a man married to a woman with an alcoholic parent (10) are married to a nurse or social worker (11) always got good grades in school—then you might say you've "had it." The statistics have turned up people in all of these categories as being more likely than others to become alcoholic. (I remembered my own Irish heritage.) If you're in one or more of those categories, you're bucking the statistics. But if you are an Orthodox Jew or are Chinese, maybe you can relax; those groups are not prone to alcoholism. (Though we had patients in Smithers from both of these groups.)

Obviously, predictions by statistics alone can often become ridiculous. One poor kid in my Smithers class groaned that he might as well give up then. He was second-generation Irish, had an Indian grandfather, had quit school in the second grade, was a Catholic, and was about to marry a Jewish nurse who had an alcoholic father. I could see why he landed in Smithers, but as far as I know he's still sober.

The fact is, alcoholism strikes anywhere, and no one is safe. Anyone who feels smug and complacent had best get over it fast, because alcohol is a sneaky drug, and some other chemicals (tranquilizers, for one) are even sneakier. And the addict usually becomes an addict without noticing.

I had little trouble applying the facts on alcoholism to my pill addiction. Gloria, on the other hand, continued to complain: She was not an alcoholic—what did all those facts have to do with her? We all tried, in vain, to explain the disease of addiction to Gloria.

Evening lecture, the Smithers version of entertainment, treated us to guest speakers from all over. On Monday and Friday nights we had simulated AA meetings or, occasionally, Al-Anon meetings. Al-Anon is a group formed by those who have family members or other loved ones who are alcoholics. It is intended to protect the lives of those who must live with, work with, or otherwise cope with, the alcoholic.

Al-Anon members are taught that, while they cannot control anyone's alcoholism, they can have some control over how that alcoholism will affect (or hopefully, not affect) them.

At one meeting, a woman member of the Smithers staff spoke. I was impressed that she was not only a recovered alcoholic, but was also a member of Al-Anon, the better to protect herself from her actively drinking husband. I listened as she recounted her life with her man. She said she was not going to judge whether he was or wasn't an alcoholic. She was, however, going to remain apart from his drinking and she was not going to let it affect her own sobriety. She would not make excuses for him when he wanted her to telephone his office and say that sickness (not hangover) was keeping him home that day. She would no longer undress him if he came home loaded. By the same token, she would not tell him that he was a drunk, nor would she urge him to reform. She did not intend to divorce him, but she would not aid and abet him in alcoholism. Most of all, she would not let his alcoholism affect her own recovery. It all sounded sensible, and relevant, to me. Alan drank heavily, and I was getting more and more pressure from my group to break up ur relationship, but it was a relationship I didn't want to lose. I made a mental note to investigate Al-Anon.

One evening a hospital pathologist came to speak, bringing with him hideous slides that would show us the ravages of alcohol in living color. There were livers with cirrhosis and pancreases with pancreatitis and, worst of all, wet brains. "Wet brain" isn't just a derogatory term applied to those who have gotten a bit wiggy from too much booze. Wet brains are literally wet. With continuing, and enormous, intake of alcohol, brain cells die off, the brain shrinks in size and is surrounded by the cranial fluid. Or at least, that's it as best I understood—or wanted to understand—it. It's a gruesome thing, and the slides were ghastly, but I stared in ghoulish fascination. Others couldn't look at all, and some were sick. All of us began to feel fairly nervous about the condition of our own innards. The pathologist asked me to describe the pain of pancreatitis, for, as he succinctly put it, most of his patients were corpses, and therefore not susceptible to pain!

About once a week our chief, Dr. LeClair Bissell, came to call—and to talk. The organizer of Smithers and its guiding force, she was small, quiet, determined, and tough. If anyone ever took liberties with the chief, I never saw it. If they did, they obviously weren't around to talk about it. Dr. Bissell fascinated everybody. She always strode in determinedly, wearing her pedometer, as if she'd just hiked in from a conference in some distant city. She called us "troops," which always brought forth rueful giggles. We felt like troops, all right—battle scars and all.

Bissell's lectures were always attended cheerfully by her troops. She was the most fascinating speaker in the place, and my notes on her lectures ran to pages. The first (and double-starred) item in those notes was the sentence "We are all responsible for our own addictions." I hadn't given much thought to responsibility before that—I was too involved with getting un-addicted. But responsibility was big on Dr. Bissell's importance list. "You are responsible," we were told—for our lives, for our addictions, and for our recoveries. And the responsibility for our recovery involved learning the facts about the enemy—drugs and booze.

40

The Smithers staff seemed to know about everything we did. When
commented one day to Gloria that one of our friends seemed inord
nately happy and was, I figured, either drunk, high, or stoned, I w
paged within minutes and told to report to the nurses' station. "We he
you think Alice is drunk." I didn't deny it. (It's odd what the brai
washing does to your sense of loyalty. By then, my loyalties were wi
the Smithers staff, and to this day, I won't protect a secret drunk.) I w
asked to describe Alice's behavior, tell whom she'd been hanging o
with, and say whether she'd disappeared to the basement, etc. Fiftee
minutes later, I heard Alice being paged on the intercom. I gather the
never mentioned my name, for Alice's behavior toward me remaine
the same. I never did find out whether she really had been drunk.

The Smithers staff seemed to know all of our secrets, though the
regularly denied that the rooms were bugged. We were sure they we
and spent hours looking for the devices but we never found a thin
Still, remarks we made to each other in the privacy of our palatial batl
room always ended up on somebody's chart. How did the staff kno
about them? Nobody knew.

Digestion was a big thing with us. Everybody was constipated. Lack of exercise does not make for regular bowel movements, and while few came right out and discussed the situation, we all drank prune juice all the time. (The Smithers staff positively sneered at requests for laxatives.) Prune juice became an in-house joke, and everyone could tell the state of everyone else's digestion by the juices he or she drank. Pretty soon we all began to develop a tolerance for prune juice, and so apple juice was discovered. It was just like switching to a new drug—instant effect! Everybody began drinking apple juice on the rocks and wearing the benevolent smiles of those whose bowel habits are "regular."

I was learning a lot about my body in Smithers. I was learning how it could function without medicine. In the past, I traveled with all of my pills. And I never, *never* went anywhere without medication for both constipation and diarrhea. It was typical addict behavior. I never waited to *see* whether anything would go wrong. I always wanted to be prepared. Now, being prepared is wonderful when it is not carried to neurotic extremes, but traveling with a suitcase full of pills "just in case" *is* neurotic in the extreme. And the preparedness must have been self-fulfilling, because I always ended up needing one of those medicines. (Could my subconscious have arranged it?) But in Smithers there were *no* medicines.

And so one day, when I'd practically overdosed on apple juice the night before (yes, I can even be addicted to nonaddictive substances), I developed a whopping case of diarrhea. Naturally I expected the nursing staff to do something. They appraised me with cool eyes and asked, "How long has this been going on?"

"A couple of hours."

"Come back tonight."

But by "tonight" my diarrhea was cured, all on my body's own. There is a moral for everyone. Before you *do* something, wait. See whether your body will take care of the problem without any help from your medicine chest. Chances are, it will.

It snowed heavily in March, and it seemed everybody had a cold. I pulled a leg muscle. What did Smithers do for us? Not much!

Headache? Take a heating pad and hold it to your head. Stomach-ache? Take a heating pad and hold it to your stomach. Pulled leg muscle? Go sit in a hot tub and then take a heating pad. . . . A cold? Wait.

"Priscilla" got a toothache and was taken to the dental clinic at the hospital. The cause was diagnosed as six infected teeth that had to come out. But Priscilla got nothing stronger than Tylenol, which gave no relief from the pain. His operation was scheduled for two days later. Priscilla moped about and held ice packs to his jaw; he threatened and cajoled—all to no avail. I have to confess that it seemed to me they were taking rigidity to the point of sadism. A toothache after all, is no joke. But Tylenol was all Priscilla got until the operation.

We all learned something from our little head-against-the-wall battles with the medical department. We learned for sure that we were not going to be given any painkillers. We also learned, to our surprise, that we could live with pain. And, most important, we learned that pain does go away—eventually.

Lately I've heard a lot about a medical theory that claims that the best medicine practiced is the medicine of noninterference. It seems that the body will usually set things right all by itself, providing it is given a chance to do so. Our society, however, is so accustomed to the common medical practice of "doing something" that we feel it is always necessary to help nature along by medical means. Giving medicine is "doing something," and many doctors (and patients) feel they aren't doing their jobs if they aren't prescribing medicine. The doctors who subscribe to the noninterference theory believe that the "doers" are the ones doing the harm, and that we would all be better off if we left a lot to nature.

I found that the leg muscle I'd pulled healed with heat therapy, Priscilla lost six teeth but nothing more, and everybody's cold eventually disappeared. We all got well without any help from the Smithers staff. I take that back—with a lot of help from the Smithers staff, who showed us the way to nonmedication.

41.

I'd been in Smithers nearly three weeks. That meant Sigrid would soon be leaving, and I counted the passing days, as if by so doing I could slow them down. Sigrid was my closest friend. She was the roommate I huddled with when the others were driving me wild. By day, Gus and I were inseparable but in the evenings, it was Sigrid who helped me survive. Now she was making preparations to rejoin the human race. And to leave me behind.

Sigrid and her "graduation class" were involved in activities that were completely mysterious to the rest of us. They were locked in secret conclaves with counselors, worked on unknown somethings, spoke in a lingo I did not comprehend, and studied silently with one another. Sigrid and her group would leave in a mass exodus. I never quite understood how it was that an entire, large group should disappear all at once, but so it was. And it seemed this time all the old and "good" crowd would be leaving. The sophisticates who had known the ropes long before I arrived. The "fun" crowd. The rest of us examined one another and were not sure we wanted only each other for company. We were not yet privy to the mysteries of graduation.

In group we had confrontations that left us in tears, while real-life dramas continued to confront us all. Patients freaked out at the idea of returning to the real world outside and some were sent off to halfway houses for more time and more cure. Marriages broke up, jobs were lost, and another patient was dismissed from Smithers. We never really understood why. The staff said she wasn't levelling with her group. She said she was. They said she had secrets she hadn't told. She said she didn't. They said she had to go. She said she wouldn't. But she did. She said she'd come back to visit. But she didn't.

And that's how it went every day. Every day of the week, except Sunday, somebody left. Some left by "graduation," others gave up and left, taking with them charts marked "Against Medical Advice." Some went unnoticed, while others left visible voids in our ranks. Nothing was ever constant, and friends were hard to keep because they were always "going to leave." And Sigrid was leaving and she was ecstatic, while I was depressed.

Just as I was beginning to feel more secure about my eventual improvement, I got a letter from my father. It began "Good luck and goodbye." I began to tremble.

"Since you say you are so miserable," the letter continued, "and you are going to leave Smithers, then I see that you are determined to destroy your life. I wish I could make you see that your only chance for getting well is to stay, to try to understand that you need help. But since you're throwing that chance away, I'm going to give up and let you do it your way. Good luck and goodbye."

Had it been another time, a place that was not Smithers, then I would have done the obvious thing. I would have taken a tranquilizer.

Now I had to react in another way. I took up my pen and began a long letter explaining to my father that what I had (imprudently, I realized) said to him—that I wanted to leave Smithers—was what we all said every day. Yes, I wanted to leave all right. But I hadn't. And I implored him to be patient, to try to understand, to know that I wanted—desperately—to be well. But it was very, very hard.

I mailed the letter and waited.

Within a few days, he phoned. "I just felt I had to make you see," he said, "that you *must* stay where you are. I thought maybe you needed the shock. You know I love you."

And, for the first time since the letter arrived, I did.

My agent telephoned one day. Was I OK? Hanging in. Did I want to sell my book? What?! Yeah, an editor had liked the outline and wanted to buy it. Granted, they weren't offering six figures, but it was a hefty five. Did I want to do it? God, yes! Did I ever! "Of course, John, tell her yes!"

And when I put down the phone I wondered whether what they'd been telling us was really true—that, miraculously, things always got better, once you got sober.

While my own mini-dramas were taking place, other, real, dramas were being enacted all the time. Take the case of Lucille. The beautiful wife of a well-known New York restaurateur, Lucille was led into Smithers by her two daughters. She looked like a zombie. Lucille was a Valium victim, I was told. Naturally, I was elected to show her the ropes. Her room was in the basement, and it held eight patients. That did not seem to bother Lucille; indeed, nothing seemed to bother Lucille. She was beyond worrying. During her intermittent periods of lucidity, she compared withdrawal symptoms with me. She was frightened out of her wits, though it was difficult to tell whether her widened eyes were due to fear or addiction. I tried to reassure her that within the week all would be well, or on the way to being well. It didn't do a lot of good. Lucille remained as fearful as ever, shook a lot, and stared into space. She spent a lot of time taking her pulse. At meals, she picked at her food and said she couldn't swallow. (It was a feeling I remembered well.) And then one day at breakfast, she looked me straight in the eye and said, "You forgot to give me my cereal."

"Huh?" I said.

"You forgot to give me my cereal," she repeated. And she continued to eat the cereal that was before her.

That was a hint of things to come. That night, seven ladies were sleeping soundly in their basement beds when Lucille stood up in the middle of the room, announced that she couldn't find her bed, and proceeded to crawl in with one of the seven. The frightened roommates rushed to the nurses' station to report trouble and Lucille was gently led away to the psychiatric ward at Roosevelt Hospital. Courtesy of Valium—and a lot of other drugs she hadn't told me about. The Smithers staff, as usual, knew about them all.

42.

By the start of my third week at Smithers, I was fat, sassy, and relatively content. With the inexplicable and uncanny resilience that human beings have, I had, it seemed, adjusted. I slept as well as could be expected with Maxine for company. And I ate and grew fatter, while it got harder and harder to zip my jeans. Sigrid, of course, never lost her model figure, but Gloria, sans amphetamines, expanded to 150 pounds. Priscilla Pocketbook lost his seductive snake shape and began to look more and more like a paterfamilias. Everyone weighed in every day on Billy Rose's custom-made, built-in-the-floor scales and by now everybody weighed twenty pounds more than when they arrived. We all complained but we all continued to eat. Somebody's mother brought in a picnic supper of fried chicken, homemade potato salad and fresh apple pie. It was demolished in minutes. There was a heated discussion between the stockbroker and the surgeon over whether or not Famous Amos was the best available brand of chocolate chip cookie. And the priest made a deal to trade me pretzels for caramel-covered popcorn. I was glad the outside world couldn't get a glimpse of our deep and intellectual discussions on the subject of food.

As Easter approached, I got nervous. Never, for as long as I could remember, had I missed Mass on Easter Sunday. Almost never did I miss it on any Sunday, for that matter, but Good Friday, Palm Sunday, and Easter were especially important to me. We were told that we could apply to our counselors for permission to attend church. I approached Anna warily. Anna was immovable. Permission to attend Good Friday services was, I was told, out of the question. Permission to attend Palm Sunday services was also denied. Easter, we would think about. It would depend on me. I was distraught. I explained that my religion was important to me and that it was inconceivable that I should be denied religious services. Besides, I was on the vestry of my church . . . I was expected to attend . . . I wanted to attend. And Anna pointed out that being deeply religious hadn't prevented me from becoming a junkie. It was probably not the religious experience that would cure me. There would be other Palm Sundays and Good Fridays and Easters long after I was cured. For now, permission was denied. Except maybe for Easter. We would talk about that later. Nothing I could say would change her mind. And so, depressed, I watched Palm Sunday come and go, just like any other Sunday.

Becky's sobs woke us. She was moaning and crying uncontrollably. It wasn't at all like Becky, the sleepy one. Usually, she never stirred, from the moment she pulled the covers over her head until we pulled them off in the morning. Becky would sleep all day if we let her. Now it was four in the morning, and Becky was weeping. Gloria and I leaped out of bed and across the room, arriving simultaneously. Becky was in pain. She was holding her stomach, rocking back and forth, and crying. Gloria ran for the nurse while I held on to Becky, who kept sobbing, "I've got cramps. . . . I can't stand the cramps." I'd never heard Becky complain before. I rubbed her head and held on to her until the nurse came.

She was the tiny, Irish nurse, the one with the soothing voice. She led Becky away, gently, to the nurses' station and called Roosevelt Hospital.

Becky was going to be hospitalized, and I was to accompany her through the ordeal of being admitted. I was almost a "senior" now—they could trust me. But they would trust me for two hours only. I must make sure I was back within that time.

I pulled on my one respectable going-out outfit—sweater, pants, and decent shoes—I felt strangely "dressed up" after a month of jeans and sneakers. And, with Becky holding on to my arm as if her life depended on it (in a way, it did), we left Smithers.

It was a brilliantly sunny late March day. Cold but sparkling. I felt as if I had never been outdoors before. We hailed a cab and Becky never let go of my hand as we sped through Central Park toward the hospital.

New York had never looked like this before—at least not for years. It looked clean, and sunny, and busy, and cheerful. Where were all the dirty streets I had complained about? Where were all the depressed people? Whether it was the promise-of-springtime morning, or what, I didn't know, but New Yorkers looked happy and purposeful as they rushed about—off to jobs, wheeling babies, jogging. New York looked good! I vowed that when, praise God, I got out of Smithers, I would walk every single one of those streets I was barely glimpsing from the speeding cab. I would explore the West Side, I would try out those restaurants, I would check out the museums, I would see the shows at the Planetarium. I would do all the things I had done, with such enthusiasm, when I first came to New York. Things I hadn't done since. I was going to *enjoy* my city. I swore I was going to enjoy life!

Soon we were at Roosevelt, and my heart sank as I walked, once more, through those familiar doors. It had not been long since I had walked (with a lot of help from Alan) out of them and into Smithers. Becky was crying into her fistful of Kleenex. I was trying to soothe her and keep my equilibrium at the same time. I was not happy about being in Roosevelt Hospital.

We sat in the waiting room for what seemed like hours before a young female gynecologist came to fetch Becky. I was told to wait. I had nothing to do but sit and read the posters on the walls that told expectant mothers all about proper nutrition. I noted wryly that the information had never been passed along to the Smithers cooks, who drew their repertoire from the carbohydrate side of the charts.

Finally the doctor appeared and told me that Becky would be admitted and that I would not be needed. Becky had disappeared into the mysterious depths of Roosevelt. The doctor assured me she was OK and signed my Smithers pass. I set out to return to Smithers alone.

The trip back was far too fast. We drove up through the park, where cherry blossoms and apple blossoms and pear blossoms made the park almost unbearably beautiful (and made me desperate to be outdoors, out of my prison). Then we were at Ninety-third Street and I walked through the doors once more and they closed behind me. Once more.

We wouldn't know about Becky for three days.

With Sigrid leaving I was tense. I didn't know what life would be like without my mentor and I didn't know what it would feel like to be the senior member of our room. I desperately tried not to think about it at all, in hopes it wouldn't happen. Sigrid was not often around, as she was closeted in meetings with her counselor and with the bookkeeper and in groups with names like "Re-Entry Group." I could only guess what they were all about. About coping on the outside, I imagined. We all kept asking the "seniors" what was going on, but they were evasive and generally returned from sessions with tears in their eyes, saying only that it was "an experience." Everybody in our room was nervous about losing Sigrid and worried about Becky. Gloria, whose three weeks without amphetamines had left her with rubbed-raw nerves, talked incessantly and began to grate on my nerves like fingernails on a blackboard. We were all on short-fuses. On one of those awful Sunday nights, Gloria and I got into an argument about whether we should sleep with the window open or closed.

Suddenly Gloria came out of bed like a panther on the attack, screaming at full lung power in language I didn't think even Gloria knew. The others shouted for her to shut up but she just kept going. "You bitch, you think you can tell me what to do?" and on and on.

The next morning nothing had changed. Gloria followed me around like a wild woman, screaming through breakfast, throwing her dishes to the floor, yelling her way back upstairs and making herself heard from the third floor to the first. The rest of the patients were aghast. I was dumbfounded, and I decided it would be discreet to stay out of Gloria's way for a while. By that night, Gloria was as friendly as if nothing had ever happened. Nobody knew what had gotten into her; nobody knew what made her recover. I chalked it up to withdrawal madness. I knew how that madness felt.

My lawyer sent me flowers. Everybody was impressed, and they brightened up the room not just for us, but for my therapy group as well. The beautiful spring flowers were a sign that Easter was almost here. Then Gloria got flowers from her husband and somebody else got some, and my mother sent a bouquet and so did my father. The room looked like a funeral home, but we were thrilled by all the attention.

And we were depressed because Sigrid had left. She had simply packed her bags the night before, kissed everybody, and left. We felt lost without her authoritative presence. Now Gloria and I were the "oldest" people in our room. We forgot our past differences and clung to each other again.

Anna, my counselor, had an accident. She slipped on the ice and broke her kneecap. She would be gone for two weeks. Not only was I without a counselor—I didn't have permission to get out on Easter Sunday. Bob de Vere, I was told, would be my counselor. I pursued him, but Bob was evasive. He would let me know about Sunday. Finally, by Friday afternoon, I resolved to pin him down, feeling that I would have to give up on Easter. It didn't seem right. Gloria fussed and fumed about having to miss church herself, but she had never gotten around to applying for permission to go out, so she was stuck. Finally, de Vere stuck his head out of his office door and said, "Easter's OK." I was excited. It would be my first time out of those doors alone. But, it was understood, I would have one hour and one hour only. I didn't know what to do—the church service always lasted two hours. I pleaded for longer. Well, one and a half hours. No more.

Easter Sunday was a washout, the first rainy Easter I'd seen in years. Never mind; nothing was going to keep me in Smithers on this day. I'd arranged to meet a friend for the service, sort of as reassurance to the authorities that I wouldn't spend Easter morning in a bar. But, throughout the entire Mass, I was inwardly panicking and outwardly watching the clock. I doubt that I really got much religion on that festival day, but I got out and I got a second look at the real world and this time I felt scared. Nothing looked normal. The street where I lived looked like somebody else's street, not mine. The incense in the church seemed stronger, the colors brighter, the people different. I felt as if I'd been away for a long, long time. I had—for three long weeks. But the outside world, strangeness, rain, and all, never seemed more compelling. I resolved silently to return to that world and I promised never again to complain about it. I would not, I vowed, ever complain about anything at all. Just let me out! Please!

43.

The next morning I felt a twinge of unexplained terror. And then I remembered. In exactly seven days I would be released from Smithers. And I had no idea what my life would be like in the real world, after Smithers.

All of us in my graduating class felt the same way. Gloria was chattering nonstop. Becky was still away and we grew apprehensive about her. Gus was dogging my footsteps, and I found myself growing impatient with his seeming dependence on me. The card-playing crowd still played cards, but their attention span was no more than an hour, and I could hear the arguments all the way to the third floor. All of the seniors were edgy. We all felt the same way—scared.

We were told to expect to be called into sessions with our counselors, with the psychologist, and with Bob de Vere, for with Bob we were to 'take the Fourth Step." We knew that referred to the AA Step that said: "Make a searching and fearless moral inventory of ourselves." And all of these sessions were to take precedence over anything else we were doing at the time. Whether we were in lecture, group, or washing our hair, we were to drop it and rush to the prescribed meeting. It sounded fearsome.

I waited to hear my name called, hoping they would start alphabetically and get to me early. But nobody, apparently, wanted to meet with me.

I was once again thinking about leaving. My rationale was that in a week I would be out anyway, so why not now? Hadn't I learned all that I was going to learn? My group said "No!" (And, in my heart, I knew "no.") But I wondered just the same.

Gloria, too, wanted to leave. Gloria was arguing with her husband and fighting with her father, who, every time he got drunk, called and told her to get out of "that place." And then Gloria would have another stomach attack, for which she still could get no medicine. The attitude of the nursing staff was not going to soften just because we were leaving.

There was, however, just the very slightest sign of softening in the rest of the staff. They smiled at us a bit. They seemed (I thought) to be developing a tiny bit more confidence in us, the seniors, as if they thought we might make it after all. Nobody ever said so. But there was a warmth seeping through the frosty exteriors of the counselors. Well, we liked to think so.

I had become the *doyenne* of Smithers, the senior of seniors, housemother to the boys, the oldest sex symbol in the place. Having a twenty-one-year-old call me "neat" and "sexy" and "beautiful" did plenty for my ego, even though I knew it wasn't true. It was because they were fond of me and I was an old-timer and, in Smithers, even the kids respected the old-timers. Suddenly it seemed sort of nice to be a senior—respected, admired, imitated—and I reveled in every minute of my newfound adulation. I needed it, too, because Alan was becoming more remote. I knew it was because soon he must face life with me once again. And neither he nor I knew what that life would be like.

I got a call on the intercom: Go to the accountant's office. (Who knew there was an accountant, much less where he hung out?) I found him in the upper reaches of the top floor, in a wing I hadn't even known existed. (And we thought we had searched for Billy Rose's millions in every nook and cranny!) The accountant turned out to be a young Oriental I'd glimpsed only briefly at the elevator. One of the several mystery people around Smithers. After he made me sign my life away (or its equivalent), agreeing to pay the bill if insurance and all else failed, we compared notes on occult books for the next hour while my group sat in their regular session two floors below. I felt like a school kid out on a good-behavior pass.

Gloria had seen her counselor and had returned in a rage, intermittently spewing out profanities and weeping copiously. It took a while to find out what had gone on. Sobbing and swearing, she told us that they didn't want her to go home. Her counselor was recommending a halfway house for three more months. Gloria, outraged, had refused to go, and now the counselor was threatening her with an AMA dismissal. Against Medical Advice.

That was serious. Against medical advice meant the insurance company probably wouldn't pick up the Smithers tab. Gloria was trapped. And she was furious. She raved on and on . . . How *dare* they suggest she would take more pills? How *dare* they suggest she couldn't go on to a normal life? How *dare* they suggest she shouldn't see her father? And how dare, dare, *dare* they suggest she go to AA? She was no alcoholic! She was on pills, and she would drink if she chose!

It had never occurred to me that Gloria intended to drink. I guess I saw pill addiction only from my own experience. I had been a drunk first, a pill junkie later. I knew I couldn't drink. But, Gloria maintained —insisted—that she had never had a problem with booze. Therefore, it was perfectly safe for her to drink, because she *always* stopped with two glasses of wine. Oh, well, yes, she drank Scotch. But she never drank much. Well, so she *had* said she'd had a hangover that time after the party. But it only happened once. Well, not very often.

Gus, in his inimitable step-on-the-sore-toe way, said, "Damn it, Gloria, you're a fucking alcoholic like the rest of us." Gloria, enraged, refused to talk to Gus. I was reluctant to reason with Gloria. For one thing, it was impossible. Gloria never shut up long enough to listen to what I was saying. To what anyone was saying.

Right in the middle of Gloria's tantrum I had a call to report to the nurse. God knew what this was! I took the stairs three steps at a time, wearing my most conciliatory smile, in deference to the cranky head nurse. I was told to sit down. To be told to sit down at Smithers meant something serious was afoot. It was Becky. Becky would not be coming back; she was very ill. I was dumbfounded. Becky had had cramps, yes —but seriously ill? And then they told me—Becky had been pregnant. Not even she had known. And then she had lost her child. She had miscarried right after I left her at the hospital. She was heartbroken, for even though she couldn't care for the children she had, Becky loved to have children. Now she would have no more children. I was thinking that was a blessing all around. And then the nurse told me Becky had found a bottle of rubbing alcohol left by a careless aide, and she did what any alcoholic would have done: she drank it.

They had managed to save her, but once she recovered she would be going away. We were not going to see her again. I was to pack her things.

And so Becky disappeared completely, before any of us ever had time to fathom the event. We never saw nor heard of her again.

On Tuesday afternoon I got a call from Carol, the psychologist. She was going to give me the results of all my testing. I wasn't so sure I wanted to know.

The first thing I learned from Carol was that my reasoning powers were still intact. I was one of the lucky ones. I hadn't irreparably damaged my brain, no matter how confused I might feel.

They had tested us for that. Reasoning power, it seems, is one of the first things to go, when alcohol or drug abuse is the issue. Memory survives a bit better. The test consisted of words to be identified on one page, problems to be solved on another. It was our ability to solve those simple problems that would tell Smithers whether or not we were on our way to "wet brain." Thankfully, my brain was not yet damp.

And then there was another test—one that had told her (and me) how dissatisfied or satisfied I was with my lot in life at that moment. When I read back over that test today, I marvel at how very much my outlook on life has changed. Here are some of the questions, with the answers I gave then:

Q: How satisfied are you with your current occupational status?
A: Very dissatisfied.
Q: How satisfied are you with your current living situation?
A: Very dissatisfied.
Q: How satisfied are you with your present health?
A: Satisfied.
Q: How often have you felt unusually fatigued or tired?
A: Almost always.
Q: How often have you felt yourself to be discouraged or depressed?
A: Frequently.

It wasn't a cheerful outlook on life, but then, I didn't feel cheerful at the time.

It is difficult for me to reconstruct my meeting with Carol. She told
me I had unrealistic goals. And that it was natural for a woman of my
age—i.e., facing middle age—to feel depressed about it. Good God! I
hadn't even thought about middle age. Wasn't I still young?

And she went on: I was depressed. Unable to deal with reality effec-
tively. Held unrealistic views of myself.

I left feeling as low as low. There was lots to think about. Like middle age.

My name was called for a Re-Entry Group on Wednesday afternoon
at three. It sounded like something NASA dreamed up. I guess getting
us all back to earth and reality presented somewhat the same problem
NASA had with spacemen. "Spaced-men" was what we were, all right.
Freaked. The group would last until four-thirty at least.

We had been divided into two re-entry groups. Gloria, who'd arrived
the day after I did, was not in my group. (I silently thanked God for
that.) Mine consisted of the priest, the dope-shooting surgeon, the loud-
mouthed salesman, two young men who were so silent they faded into
the woodwork, the still toothless "cowboy" who'd lived on the streets,
two black Welfare mothers, the brain-damaged enigma from my group,
a distinguished-looking, secretly homosexual stockbroker, a nondescript
Valium-addicted housewife, and me. And our Re-Entry Group leader,
Peggy.

We all sat around, silent and apprehensive, except for the salesman,
who launched into his "cute" routine, and the surgeon, who sullenly
slouched on the sofa and closed his eyes. The toothless cowboy stood
near the door. He was asked to take his seat. He refused. Peggy
insisted. And then he exploded. Shouting his gummy profanity, the cowboy screamed that he wasn't going to take any more orders from anybody. Nobody would tell him he had to sit when he wanted to stand.
And he whirled and slammed out of the room, banging Billy Rose's big
paneled door behind him.

The rest of us had our jaws hanging open. Peggy remained unruffled
and looked around the room as if to size up the group, then launched
into her re-entry spiel. She wanted to know what our plans were for
maintaining our sobriety and how we intended to carry them out.

I dreaded the moment when Peggy would call on me. I somehow always equated being called on with being called down. As if I'd done
something wrong. And I really didn't know what my plans were, so

that instead of concentrating on the problems of the others, I was worrying about what to say when Peggy got around to me.

The salesman began. This time he had learned his lesson. This time he knew he was truly an alcoholic. This time he would do things differently. This time he wouldn't drink. This time he would be honest with himself and others. This time he would get a job. This time he wouldn't lie. This time he would get well. And Peggy said, "You're full of shit." We all sat up.

It was what we had all felt like saying, and more than we had expected from Peggy. The salesman shut his loud mouth while Peggy proceeded to tell him that he wasn't being honest, that he hadn't really tried, that his patter was merely that—patter. She said that he wore a sign on his rear end that said, "Kick Me," and that, if he continued in his present behavior, that was what the world would do. And when it did, he would drink. The salesman sputtered a bit and said nothing. We prayed he had been permanently quashed. At least for the moment he seemed abashed.

The stockbroker was depressed. He hadn't been helped very much, he said. He needed to see his shrink.

The brain-damaged boy was asked to say what he intended to do upon his discharge. He grinned and stared at the ground and was silent. We were all silent.

Around the room she went. The Welfare mothers wanted jobs, apartments, men to help care for their children. One of the nondescript young men wanted Smithers to find him an apartment. The other wanted Smithers to get his job back.

Smithers wouldn't help get any of those things. Smithers would get us sober and that was all. The rest would be up to us. But Smithers would always be interested in what, in fact, we *did* do.

And then I heard myself saying that my plans were to follow Anna's suggestions—whatever they turned out to be. I didn't know about the rest. I hoped to work. I had a book to write. I would try to do that.

Miraculously, Peggy seemed satisfied. (Either that, or she found my answers too boring to be worth further investigation.) There were one or two more questions, some admonishments to attend AA meetings. We were told once more that Smithers would always be there to help when we needed help. And we were dismissed. We filed out to re-enter Smithers. We couldn't tell if we were ready to re-enter the real world.

44.

Sigrid called. She was home and she was unhappy. Her husband was boring and her lover was unavailable and she was jumpy. Oddly enough, Sigrid missed her Smithers friends. As a matter of fact, we were about the only friends she had. We missed Sigrid, too, and we all took turns at the pay phone telling her all the gossip of the post-Sigrid period. And then she rang off with the promise to visit. She didn't.

Gus was grumpy. He was going to lose me and in losing me he was going to lose his constant companion, friend, mentor and would-be love. Gus was a ticking time bomb.

Gloria was still sulking, though she had begun to pour out her problems to me. She *knew* she had been hooked on pills. But she knew she was off them now. (Hearing her voice, running on at full clip, I wondered when she would stop flying.) She hated, *hated* her counselor and would kill him if she could. She *dreaded* facing her alcoholic father on the outside because she *knew* (now she *realized*) that it would give her a stomach attack. She *wondered* (I knew she *knew*) about her husband —was he, *could* he be homosexual? (I said I didn't know.) And she *knew* she was no alcoholic like the rest of us and she'd be *damned* if she wouldn't drink. Hell! Without pills *or* booze, how did they expect her to survive?

At two o'clock on Friday afternoon, I sat in Anna's office for the last time, waiting, with the mixed emotions of relief and dread, to hear her recommendations for my post-rehab treatment. I wasn't sure I wanted to hear them at all, but one thing I knew . . . I didn't dare leave Smithers without a support system, ready and waiting.

"If I thought you could afford it," Anna began, "both the money and the time—I would insist that you go to a halfway house. Specifically, Alina Lodge." My heart dropped. That was where they wanted to send Gloria. "But I know you have a deadline to meet and so I am going to recommend outpatient treatment at Roosevelt."

I spent an hour with Anna, going over all the aspects of my new life at home. It was, it seemed, going to be very new. New and possibly frightening. My reactions to things would not be the same as they had been. My perceptions would be different. My nerves were going to be "rubbed raw." I was not, repeat *not,* under any circumstances to make any changes in my life at this time. But, I interrupted, I didn't think I could stay with Alan. I didn't think he wanted me, he wasn't ready to marry me, I was tired of wasting my time, and besides, he drank.

No, I was not to leave Alan at this time.

"But I hate my apartment and I want to move."

"You cannot move at this time."

"But I'm uncomfortable in my apartment. I have a sofa I can't even sit on!"

"You'll give the sofa to charity and take a tax loss."

Anna had practical answers for everything. She warned me that all would be lost if I shook up my life just now. Everything was to come to a standstill for one whole year. By then—just maybe by then—I would have my head together enough to make rational decisions. Though she couldn't guarantee it.

She assured me that my withdrawal could continue for a minimum of six months. At this time I could hope for some respite. Pill withdrawal is difficult. It is the reason that halfway houses are recommended for pill patients. The withdrawal is often so bad that patients tend to return to their former pill habits, just because they can't take those withdrawal pains.

Group therapy was recommended, especially since my work kept me isolated much of the time. To further combat the isolation of writing,

Anna advised me to keep my television set on most of the time. Not a radio, but a TV. For the illusion of company in the room.

And then, having given me the name of my therapist-to-be at Roosevelt, with instructions to call her for an appointment as soon as I got home, Anna wished me luck and said good-bye. She reminded me that I could call on her for help at any time . . . and she left the room.

People were beginning to freak out. The surgeon was no longer smug and smiling, but depressed and dismal. He was beginning to wonder, he said, whether or not he still had his wife, his children, his practice. He was going to take a trip to Europe the moment he was released. He hoped his habit was gone. It was, in fact, the very first time he had spoken of his habit as something that should be "gone."

The toothless cowboy took offense, that night at supper, at what he considered a slight. Someone else was sitting in his accustomed seat at the table. (It didn't matter that the someone else was someone new who didn't know any better.) The cowboy slammed from the room and, before anyone realized what happened, headed for the front door, shouting profanities at the nurses and threats at anyone who tried to stop him. And he left Smithers. Two days before his official release.

Gloria alternated between silent sulks and tirades against not only her counselor but all of Smithers. She'd be damned if she was going to call herself an alcoholic. She'd be damned if she'd give up alcohol. And she'd be damned if Smithers could tell her what to do.

Maxine had stayed away from the room, except for sleeping, ever since the big fight. But one day she appeared in the doorway—dead drunk. We prayed the Smithers counselors would see her. We knew that we weren't going to report her. It simply wasn't worth the hassle, now that we were almost free. So Maxine fell into bed at five that Friday afternoon and didn't come to until Saturday morning. For once, no one ever knew.

Sunday came. It would be my last visiting day of all time. On the phone, Alan was offhand about what time he would arrive. I thought he seemed colder, more remote than ever. He would try to get to Smithers around three-thirty. It would leave two hours' visiting time. That apparently was enough for Alan.

The newcomers were receiving their guests enthusiastically and guiding them about the house. Our shower remained the main attraction. By then I didn't give a damn how many people marched through. I was getting out!

Two of my former drinking buddies were going to visit on this last Sunday—on the condition that we would have visitors' badges for them so there'd be no question of their hard-drinking past lives catching up with them and getting them accidentally committed. We thought the idea hilarious and spent an hour after lunch cutting out little "Patient" and "Visitor" badges.

All of my visitors arrived at once, and suddenly Smithers seemed gala. Alan invited me to a "getting sprung" dinner. Friends said that as soon as I got settled, we'd all go lots of places together. Places I hadn't felt like going for some time.

I announced my plans for my first day out. I certainly wasn't going to spend it trying to lose weight. I was going to enjoy myself! Before the diet would come the banquet—a pasta dinner in my favorite Greenwich Village trattoria. I was going to treat myself just fine!

Hollywood's Academy Awards were going to be shown that very night, and I was getting out of Smithers just in time to see it in living color, after a month of sepia television. I was going to revel in the cornball colorama of it all. Tinsel time!

I had it all planned. Monday we celebrate. Tuesday we deal with sobriety.

Alan was the last visitor to leave. "I don't know if I'm going to get here tomorrow morning," he was saying, ". . . a meeting." I couldn't believe my ears. Alan wasn't going to come for me?

"Don't you know I need you? Don't you even want me to come home?" My voice had grown shrill. But Alan simply muttered he'd call me later. And he left.

That night was the lowest Sunday night of them all. I sat through the same depressing movie on alcoholism that I'd seen in Roosevelt Hospital. Everything, by now, seemed like a rerun. I was incredibly jumpy and I was furious with Alan. Didn't I matter more to him than some idiotic meeting he could've set up some other time? Didn't he give a damn that I was coming home. To him? I concluded that he didn't and felt even more depressed.

After the film we all drifted into the dining room. Even Gloria wasn't up to her usual card game. Those of us who were going to leave tomorrow or the day after went off to pack. This time for real.

I tried telephoning Alan, but his line was busy. I still felt angry. Why should his phone be busy if he wasn't calling me? Who was he calling?

Eventually, Alan called. Yes, he said coldly, he'd be there to pick me up. About ten-thirty. "Ten-thirty? Don't you know I want to get out of here? I want to go home!" His voice grew colder. "I'll be there as early as I can make it." And he hung up.

On Monday morning I was up by five forty-five, first in the breakfast line, and first out of the dining room, rushing to dress. There were things to do: retrieve my money and my credit cards, my checkbook, and whatever other things were still with the cashier. Retrieve my cologne from the nurse. Sign forms of receipt. Then rush back upstairs to say good-bye to people before lecture began. Everything went in such a whirl I didn't have much time to feel sad.

Gloria and I made plans for lunches and Gus and I made plans for trysts and we all swore we'd see each other as soon as we were all out together. Then the crowd went into lecture while I dragged shopping bags and coats and handbags and books down those spiral stairs for the very last time. I said good-bye to any staff that was around, good-bye to the nurses, good-bye to the maids and the porters, and I searched, without success, for Mel. Maybe I should go to just one more group session. . . . Just then Alan arrived. It was nine-fifteen, and while for the rest of the world another week was beginning, for me and for Alan it was the beginning of two different lives. I forgot my pique of the previous night, excitedly threw my arms around him, and was saying good-byes all around once more when Mel appeared with a big smile, a hug, and a lot of warm good-luck wishes. Then he disappeared towards his group. *My* group. Of which I would never again be a part.

Then Alan opened those huge, heavy doors, and we stepped out into a beautiful April morning.

III.

45.

I wish I could say that I walked out of Smithers straight into a perfectly normal life. Such was not to be the case. I walked out of Smithers with full knowledge of the things I must do: arrange for outpatient therapy at Roosevelt Hospital. Keep in touch.

But, on that April day, I was going to do none of those things. I was going to celebrate my new freedom.

Here is the way it went:

My doormen all greeted me warmly. They knew of my hospitalization (though of course they couldn't know why), and each solicitously inquired about my health. Welcome home! It was wonderful to be back.

Alan helped me get the huge suitcase, the tattered shopping bags, and all my accumulated litter, out of the cab and onto the doormen's trolley, and we began my journey back to my own life.

The hallway looked strange. Smaller. Trembling, I unlocked the door to my apartment and stepped inside.

My reaction was immediate and violent. Every nerve in my body was assaulted by the leaping colors, all the quivering patterns, the multihued china, the shelves of books. I felt my eyes begin to jump uncontrollably. I felt real physical pain in my limbs. It was, of course, my first reaction to sensory assault. My body, still in the acute stage of drug withdrawal, was reacting violently.

It was quite a few minutes before I could order my senses. An hour or so, in fact.

The desk was piled a foot high with stacks of unopened mail. Some of it, I saw with dismay, dated to the week before my hospitalization. The rest had been stashed there by the maid. The rest of the place looked neat and clean. I sank into the sofa, and had my first at-home cup of tea.

There were phone calls to be made. To my mother. To my father. To all my friends in town. And then to the friends still in Smithers. Gloria was itching to get out. She was to leave the following day (having finally persuaded Smithers she didn't need a halfway house) and she wanted me to tell her what it was like to be on the outside. She, too, was nervous and jumpy. I assured her that being out was simply swell.

Alan and I went for lunch and the whole world looked sunny and beautiful. I lunched on quiche and salad and savored every morsel. At the next table a couple were fighting. When the husband abruptly got up and stalked out, the woman ordered another Bloody Mary and proceeded to get wildly drunk. I couldn't take my eyes off her. She looked a mess.

Back at the apartment, I unpacked, and while putting away my makeup I looked with amusement at my medicine cabinet. It was still empty, and the maid had taken full advantage of the fact by fastidiously cleaning every vacant shelf. It looked very strange indeed.

Alan and I, our differences forgotten, were going to celebrate for real that night. I had made that promise to myself. And for my first night on the town, I planned to *do* the town. We would have that fattening pasta dinner, and then I was just going to curl up in front of my beautiful, big, true-color television to watch those awards, live from Hollywood. It was just the sort of kitsch my battered brain needed at that moment. It was going to be grand! But first, Alan and I would make love. And we did. Spectacular love.

The pasta was gorgeous, and Alan had vino while I looked on nostalgically and tried to keep the determined waiter from pouring it for me.

We strolled through the Village and I reveled in the sights and sounds, so long forgotten.

Back at home, we hooted and cackled over filmtown's peculiarities, then I kissed Alan goodnight and got ready for what was going to be the very first night in years when I would sleep—soundly in my own bed—and without a pill. I couldn't wait.

I waited a very long time. I got up and did the things they had taught me at Smithers. I drank milk. And I got back into bed to wait some more. But there was no sleep.

The room was far too bright. I was spoiled by the huge, dark, shuttered room in Smithers. Here, the reflections from the streetlights were making my room look bright as day. These hideous glass towers! I should have gotten curtains.

I watched television for an hour and then I phoned Alan, knowing that, with his insomnia, he'd still be awake.

He wasn't. But he was patient as ever. "Give yourself a little time. It's the excitement. Just lie there quietly and you'll sleep." I didn't.

By three o'clock I decided that perhaps if my bed faced a different way, the light wouldn't disturb me so. At three-fifteen I was struggling to push a four-poster around the room.

At four o'clock I was pushing it another way. I wondered whether there was anyone home downstairs and gave thanks for the fact that the Arabs were usually away

By five I began to shake all over. This couldn't be happening again. Was I really no better at all?

At six I got up and made myself tea. And then coffee.

At seven o'clock I had breakfast and read the papers.

At 8:30 A.M. I called Smithers.

I have never been so glad to hear one single voice as I was then to hear Anna's. Throaty, low, quiet, calm. Telling me exactly what to do.

"I want you to walk at least two miles today. And then get together with some of your fellow alcoholics and discuss all this with them. Ask Alan to stay with you. He should stay for as long as it takes. Make sure to eat, tonight take a very hot bath, and drink some warm milk. Tonight you will sleep. I promise you'll sleep tonight."

It would never have occurred to me not to do all these things. I phoned Alan. Would he stay? He would. I called everybody I knew in any state of alcoholism recovery. And they all swore to me: It will get better. A day at a time.

By bedtime, I was thoroughly exhausted but I did all of the other things—hot bath, hot milk—and I went to bed.

I awoke the next morning at my (by now)` usual hour of six-thirty. had, glory to God and thanks to Anna, slept. Soundly and sweetly, a home in my own bed, naturally and comfortably, without medication for probably the very first time in my adult life. I almost cried with grat itude. Perhaps I was going to be all right after all.

46.

I would like to tell you that I lived happily and healthily ever after without a problem in the world. It just wasn't so.

For one thing, I was withdrawing violently. All of the symptoms that had continued in Smithers were still with me now. Were exaggerated, in fact, by the new, varied, and multitudinous stimuli awaiting me in the outside world. I was no longer sheltered within the spacious and serene confines of the mansion on Ninety-third Street. I was out there, dealing with the hustle and the bustle of the real world. The tough, real world that is New York City.

I felt as if my skin had been turned inside out. As if I had been peeled and my hide reversed. (Sort of a human reversible coat.) The nerves were all there on the outside, with every living ending exposed and vulnerable and raw. I knew now why amputated frogs' legs could still jump when hit by a jolt of electricity. That was how I felt, jolted by every sound, every sight, everything that crossed my shaky path.

In my therapy group at Smithers, I talked about my withdrawal, how I felt mentally, how I felt physically, and I always asked for help when I felt especially bad. The old-timers all assured me that I was normal. I was going to be like that for a while. I should try to relax and know that, in about six months, it would be all over. Six months seemed to be the magic moment when withdrawal would end.

Whenever I spoke with other recovered alcoholics, every story I heard could have been my own story. I was, it seemed, a classic case of alcohol/pill addiction. But I would definitely recover.

I learned about, and began to practice, HALT, an AA acronym that stood for "Hungry, Angry, Lonely or Tired"—all things an addict should never be. The reasons are simple. Both hunger and anger are often misinterpreted by the body as signals to take a drink or a pill. And loneliness or tiredness can make anybody look for comfort in the bottle—of either booze or pills. And so the addict simply can't afford to be any of the four HALT things.

I had learned, thanks to hypoglycemia, that I just couldn't go hungry. Angry? Well, the red-headed Aries temperament was just going to have to cool down. I tried hard never to be lonely (and thanked heaven for Alan, who solicitously stayed with me much of the time) and as for tired—well, I never seemed to *be* tired anymore. There was a good physical reason for that.

It was explained to me that the brain, struggling to get through the haze of sedation, has to work twice as fast and twice as hard to get its impulses through. Therefore it puts out twice as many impulses. When the sedation is removed, the brain continues to run double-speed. That accounted for the jerkiness of the limbs, the flashing lights, the souped-up sounds, the wide-popped eyes that were all symptoms of my withdrawal. It would be at least six months (that date once more) before my whirling brain would calm down and adjust to a newly cleaned-out body. Meanwhile I would have to learn to cope.

Learning to cope was no breeze. I felt ghastly most of the time. The slightest noise made me leap from my chair. Bright light was actually painful. My eyes weren't as scarily popped, but they were wide-eyed just the same, and I still jerked. My body, racked by huge shudders running through it, would snap as if it were palsied. It was embarrassing. I fervently hoped no one noticed.

It took very little to set my withdrawal symptoms off and running at full speed. I was unable to cope with adjustments to anything at all. One day, in a moment of spring-cleaning zeal, I decided to change the position of a chair in my apartment and it was a whole week before I stopped freaking out about it. That one little difference in my surroundings set my entire mind to confusion.

I rode on the floor of taxis, much to Alan's chagrin. For one thing, they all seemed to be going ninety miles an hour and dangerously at that. I kept my fist in my mouth, in order not to scream, sat on the floor, in order not to see, and prayed a lot.

I had trouble concentrating. Newspapers were forgotten by the time I got to the final page and the only books I could handle were the most fanciful and frothy sort of fiction. My memory seemed all but gone. It was scary, but everybody assured me the memory would return in due time.

As spring progressed into summer, I continued with my twice-a-week therapy. One time alone with a counselor, another with my group. The group was made up entirely of recovering addicts—most alcoholics, some pill-heads like me. We thrashed out our mutual problems for two and a half hours per week.

I still found that little things could set me off, make the withdrawal symptoms worse. The hum of the air conditioner, signaling hot weather again, took me back to the previous year and sent me into a tailspin. Discovering some never-worn dresses I didn't remember buying (I still don't), made my arms and head jerk and my eyes ache. But, as the months wore on, it took less and less time to recover from the mini-break-outs.

I lurked in town that summer, and turned down weekend invitations, except for one with Sarah. When I felt myself getting weird, I made polite excuses and returned to the city. Mostly, Alan and I were contented with day trips in rented cars.

I was miserable with my looks. I couldn't lose the weight I had put on in Smithers. I had planned to drop those twenty pounds fast by my usual stringent and oddball dieting. I tried everything—low-calorie, low-carbohydrate, Scarsdale—but the weight stayed at 124 pounds. Depressed, I decided I would have to resign myself to it for a while. I just didn't dare put too many pressures on my otherwise battered body.

On October third, six months after I left Smithers, I wrote these words. They describe withdrawal, much more vividly than I could possibly describe it today. For the mind, in its blessed wisdom, does forget. Here is the way it felt back then:

Today is my sixth anniversary. It has been six months to the day since I emerged from the cocoon that is Smithers. The six months that were held out to me as the haven at the end of withdrawal. The moment when pain would cease and my life would return to "normal." The moment I never believed would come.

It is difficult, when one is suffering, to remember when one was no Memory plays tricks, and illness can only remember illness while pai blocks the memory of health.

And yet, today, I am here . . . six months out of Smithers, seven whol months sober. Meaning that for seven months no foreign substance has en tered my body. I am, as they say, clean and dry. Those who haven't bee otherwise cannot know the joy of feeling "pure." There is enormous satis faction in not allowing *any* medication down the gullet. About four month sober, I had a dream. Drunk dreams are normal. So are drug dreams. dreamed that someone was forcing—no, had forced—a phenobarbital dow my throat. The wailing and tearing of hair was real indeed. I screamed "Don't you realize I've been sober ninety days?!" and awoke in tears. Th agony of seeing my precious ninety-day-mark dissolve in a capsule. The ec stasy of knowing it was but a dream.

No one, who hasn't been there, can understand the terrors of withdrawal It is relentless. It is maddening. It is horror. It is, perhaps, the strongest de terrent to my ever taking a mood changer again.

Looking back on these six months, I realize that I am tough. Physicall tough, for withdrawal is the cruelest punishment that can be inflicted on th body. I am, however, not tough enough to endure it again. Once. Not twice The fear of a repeat experience makes me tough enough to avoid falling, fo it is far easier to resist pills than it is to recover again. That, I don't believe . could ever do.

It is funny how sobriety slips up on one. It is only now . . . now that I re alize the date . . . that I realize as well what has happened to me physicall in these past six months. It is incredible what the experts know. In si months, they said, I would—though I couldn't believe it then—feel better. would, they said, forget what it had been like. Today I realize that it is par tially forgotten.

When I think back it seems like someone else's nightmare. But I must tr never to forget what the living nightmare was like.

Nights without sleep that stretched into weeks with little sleep; agonizin and uncontrollable spasms of the body; a hand that leaped from my la against my will; the shudders that racked my body at unpredictable mo ments. When a noise was too loud. When the light was too bright. Havin hallucinations after two cups of coffee. Seeing flashing lights where ther were none. Seeing people where there were none. Finding myself in m apartment yet seeing nothing familiar. Staring at old friends whose face seemed not quite the same. Hearing my own voice coming from some dis tant place, from a body that could not have been my own.

Patterns of light and color whirred around in the brain and never too shape. Sidewalks rose up to meet me, stairs were never where they shoul have been and rooms became tunnels without end. Visual aberrations are a ways disturbing. In the first weeks of sobriety, visual aberrations are terrifying, and perhaps the most terrifying thing of all is the realization that visual aberrations will be part of our lives for six full months. And now the six months have miraculously passed and visual aberrations are no more. And already I must consciously bring to mind their memory. It is a memory I must never forget if I am to live. For to forget is to slip and to slip is to die.

It is the memory of months of agony that keeps me fearful of sedating myself again. Nothing that could happen to me now is terrible enough to warrant sedation. I know I must handle it myself.

"Handling it" is something I never did in my life. I listen in wonderment now to those who tell me pressures are too great for them to "handle" without the help of a drink or a pill. I am astonished at what I hear and grateful that the same is no longer true for me. And I have begun to understand the term "grateful recovered alcoholic," for I find myself wondering how I would have coped with life (*whether* I could have coped with life) had I not been forced into a confrontation between life and my own reality.

It is strange to find oneself a baby, taking first steps, at my age. And yet that is how it is. It is as if I am learning about life for the first time, taking toddler's steps as I go.

47.

One week after my release from Smithers, I was asked to appear on a radio show in my role as an author. I panicked. I had never—but *never* —appeared on *any* kind of show without first taking a drink (in *those* days) or a tranquilizer (when drinking became a no-no). I always popped something in my mouth, moments before the show began, just to make sure that I appeared cool and calm. And here I was being asked to speak publicly with absolutely no buffer between me and the world out there.

I asked my therapist for counsel. What should I do? I couldn't possibly perform un(chemically)calmed. Perhaps it would be better to forgo the whole thing, in spite of the obvious publicity benefits, until a later time. After all, my mind was still cloudy and my memory rotten. Suppose I couldn't remember what was in my very own book? Suppose I didn't know the answers to any questions? Suppose, suppose, suppose?

And my therapist said, "So, let's suppose. Suppose you don't know the answers to any questions? Suppose you can't remember what you've written in your very own book? What then?"

"Well," I said. "I'd make a positive fool of myself. And in public, too."

And the therapist said, "So what?"

"So what! Why that would be horrible!"

"Why?"

"Well, it just would!"

"What would happen?"

"Well, I guess nothing."

Which was precisely her point. Nothing was going to happen to me if I didn't know the answers to the questions. Nobody would take me out and shoot me if I didn't remember my own book. And if I looked stupid, then so what? It's not particularly pleasant to look dumb, but it sure won't kill you. And so I did the show and, believe it or not, the minute I opened my mouth, I felt calm.

My subconscious cooperated and the right answers came out. Oh, my hands were shaking and (I thought) my voice was shaking too. But friends who were listening said I sounded cool as the proverbial cucumber.

Most important of all, I learned that the therapist had been right. Absolutely *nothing* would have happened to me in any case. For the simple fact is that most fears, if we stop to examine them, are irrational. And if—when you're dreading embarrassment, or rejection, or even an attack of nerves—you stop and ask yourself, "What is the worst thing that could happen to me?" (and you answer your own question realistically), you'll find that nothing could be as bad as taking a drink or a pill. *That* is the very worst thing you have to fear, for sedation can do far worse things to your mind and body than the likes of embarrassment ever could. *Do not sedate yourself because you think you need it.* Fears can never kill you. Drugs can.

In Smithers I learned about drugs. Surprising things about drugs I had taken, drugs my friends were taking, drugs we knew were dangerous and dangerous drugs we believed were safe. (I learned, in fact, that there really is no such thing as a truly "safe" drug. Even aspirin can be deadly if misused. I'd like to pass along to you some of what I learned.

Tranquilizers are the most commonly prescribed drugs in this country today and are routinely taken not only for calming twitchy nerves, but for every ill from headache to muscle spasms. They are doled out to the tune of *hundreds of millions* of prescriptions per year. And, of those people taking these drugs, it has been estimated that at least half are in some stage of addiction. It's a damned scary picture, all those millions of addictive pills going down all those unsuspecting throats.

Tranquilizers are divided into two classifications—minor tranquilizers and major tranquilizers—and the very names cause enormous confusion.

Minor tranquilizers are the antianxiety drugs, such as Librium, Valium, Tranxene. Minor tranquilizers are so named because they are used for relatively minor problems: neurotic problems like anxiety attacks, general nervousness, and even insomnia. One of these "minor" tranquilizers, Dalmane, has become the nation's most widely prescribed sleeping pill.

But minor tranquilizers come equipped with major problems. The minor tranquilizers are the ones with the greatest addictive potential. They are truly dangerous drugs!

Sadly, they are not treated like dangerous drugs, and people who would swoon at the suggestion that they try a little heroin have no qualms at all about taking Valium, for example, three or four times a day. But minor tranquilizers are even more addictive and harder to withdraw from than that much-feared drug, heroin.

The *American Journal of Psychiatry,* in a 1977 article, issued a warning about diazepam (Valium) withdrawal, pointing out that withdrawal symptoms have been reported even in cases where small doses comprised the regimen. Meaning that if you have been taking as little as 5 milligrams of Valium per day, but taking it regularly, chances are that you may already be hooked.

Many people, of course, when they try to give up their tranquilizers, suffer the withdrawal, and believing it is only their old "anxiety" at work, return to the drug, never realizing that it is the drug itself that has become the problem. And that drug problem is going to be a lot harder to get rid of than the original anxiety.

I believe we should all be aware of the very real and very serious dangers inherent in all "minor" tranquilizers. Only then will we stop popping tranquilizers for every little nervous-making irritation. Tranquilizers (they tell me) have a legitimate use—in hospital situations and the like—but "minor" tranquilizers were never, never meant to be used under open-ended (refillable) prescriptions, for long-term therapy. No doctor can ever justify using one of those dangerous drugs for longer than a two-week period. First of all, because after that span they no longer have the desired effect, but most of all because, beyond that, the patient is probably hooked. Addicted. Which is when the real problems begin.

The major tranquilizers and the slow-acting antidepressants, on the other hand, have very little chance of addicting anyone. The major tranquilizers are the antipsychosis drugs and are used in treating illnesses like schizophrenia and paranoia. They include such drugs as Lithium Carbonate, Stelazine, and Thorazine. The slow-acting antidepressants (also known as mood elevators) include Tofranil and Elavil, and of this group Elavil is suspect. That is because it has a price on the street and so obviously is giving somebody, somewhere, some kind of kick. Lest you panic upon finding one of your own medicines listed here, let me hasten to add that it doesn't necessarily mean you're psychotic; many physicians use major tranquilizers in relieving neuroses.

One of my very own drugs, Navane—the one I took to keep my diseased thyroid from freaking out my head—is listed as a major tranquilizer. It was incredible to me that Navane, the strongest drug I took, was the only one that was nonaddictive.

Before you believe, however, that major tranquilizers are harmless drugs, let me point out that they, too, may have at least one serious and tragic side effect. The disorder these drugs can create is called tardive dyskinesia and it is a neurological disorder. A patient with tardive dyskinesia develops an uncontrollable and ugly twitch of the extremities or the whole body. Sometimes these symptoms don't appear until after the patient has been taking the major tranquilizers for years, and by then it's too late. Simply stopping the drug does not stop the symptoms, and once they've begun there's no way of telling when—if ever—they will stop. And so major tranquilizers may produce, rather than cure, a lifetime of psychological pain. In severe psychosis, the physician may have no option. But for neuroses? One wonders whether the risk is not too great.

Narcotic drugs are generally thought of as morphine and derivatives like heroin and opium. But they also include such drugs as methadone. Methadone, of course, was developed in the laboratory to wean addicts from heroin. But it was discovered, too late for some, that methadone itself is equally addictive. (It, too, is now traded "on the street.") The painkillers codeine, Percodan, Darvon, and Talwin are all strong narcotics, and never to be taken lightly.

I was surprised to see Darvon on the list of narcotics. A few years back the drug Darvon was pronounced virtually useless by the U. S. Food and Drug Administration. No more efficient than aspirin. Not *as* efficient as aspirin. I believed—and I am sure it was the common belief—that Darvon was also as innocuous as aspirin. But by November of

1978, the *New York Times* was reporting that the Health Research Group "asked the Federal Government either to ban the pain-killing drug Darvon or to limit its sales on the ground that its flagrant abuse was killing more than 1,000 Americans yearly and in some areas causing more deaths than heroin and morphine."

And they went on to quote Dr. Sidney M. Wolfe, director of the group, which is the medical branch of Ralph Nader's Public Citizen consumer interest lobby, as saying that Darvon "leads all other prescription drugs in the United States in drug-related deaths." It, too, contains a chemical related to methadone and thus to heroin.

But Darvon's problems did not end with that report. In March of 1979, researchers at Bowman-Gray Medical School in Winston-Salem, North Carolina, found that one of the ingredients in Darvon Compound, phenacetin, could be linked to urinary tract cancer. (Darvon Compound isn't the only painkiller that contains phenacetin. It's also found in Empirin Compound, which is nonprescription, and in Fiorinal.)

So much for the ineffectual, and therefore supposedly innocuous drug Darvon. We are seeing more and more often that many of the dangers don't show up until after a drug has been used for many, many years. By that time, it could be too late for the unsuspecting user.

The fact is, you simply shouldn't take a drug when you really don't have to. No doctor should prescribe a drug if the problem can be cured without it. If an illness is, in effect, self-limiting, then one should give the body time to mend itself without drug interference. And possible addiction. And possible drug death. For the ills that can result from indiscriminate drug use are many and grave and always avoidable—if you avoid drugs.

Amphetamines are dangerous, and dangerously addictive, drugs. They are "speed." They speed the body up, to the point of practically eating it alive. The bodily organs are prey to premature senility. The teeth and the hair fall out. And nobody, but nobody, on "speed" looks like anything but hell.

But amphetamines are routinely doled out to patients who want to "lose a few pounds." Patients who have no patience with being overweight. Not even for the time it takes to diet safely. After my release from Smithers, I sat in a doctor's waiting room one day, and to my horror heard the nurse casually announce, "Mrs. Watson wants thirty Dexedrine." I, in my now-nosy manner, inquired what Mrs. Watson would do with thirty Dexedrine. "She needs them," came the reply. "For what?" "For her diet. Some people need help."

Well, help in the form of "speed" is not the kind of help I hope to get from my doctor. And yet doctors do go right on administering amphetamines freely to overweight patients, knowing full well the addiction potential of that particularly dangerous group of drugs. You should be aware that practically all appetite-curbing prescription medication contains amphetamine. And you should also be aware that amphetamine is going to make you nervous, edgy, and grumpy. Eventually it may also make you dead.

Cocaine—the chic drug of the past decade—stimulates like amphetamine. So while it's messing up the insides of your nose (which it will certainly do), it is also messing up your insides. Cocaine is, quite simply, one more form of speed.

Dexedrine and Benzedrine, the old college tools for all-night exam-cramming, are the best-known amphetamines. One of the worst things about these (aside from the fact that they're dangerous in themselves) is that they allow your body to stay awake and work far past its natural exhaustion point. When the amphetamine wears off, your poor body totally gives up. You "crash" mentally and physically. (Some people crash right to the ground.) Amphetamines are simply not safe to use. Not for anything.

I'm simply going to list some of the most common drugs, in their proper categories, so that you can check off the ones you may have in your medicine chest. You ought to know what you're taking. And you ought to be aware that every one is, in its own way, a potentially dangerous drug.

Minor Tranquilizers (Antianxiety)	Major Tranquilizers (Antipsychosis)
Ativan	Lithium Carbonate
Dalmane	Mellaril
Librium	Navane
Serax	Prolixin
Tranxene	Sparine
Valium	Stelazine
	Thorazine

Barbiturates

Donnatal, which is
  atropine and
  phenobarbital
Fiorinal, which is aspirin,
  phenacetin, caffeine
  and a barbiturate
Luminal
Nembutal
phenobarbital (Elixir of
  phenobarbital, by the
  way, is phenobarbital
  combined with alcohol.
  Double whammy.)
Seconal
Tuinal

Sedative Hypnotics

chloral hydrate
Doriden
Miltown
Noludar
Placidyl
Quāālude

Narcotics

codeine
Darvon
Demerol
heroin

methadone
morphine sulphate
Percodan
Talwin

There are, of course, many, many others, but these are some of the more commonly prescribed drugs. Check the list to find out which ones (for there may be several) you are taking. Consider whether or not, knowing what you do now, you wouldn't rather throw them out. After you've discussed it with your doctor, of course.

48.

When I left Smithers, I was ecstatic about the fact that most of my very real medical problems seemed to have disappeared. Everybody asked me how it had happened. I couldn't explain. But now that I couldn't take any more migraine medication, I no longer got migraines. And the violent and vicious stomach pains (were they really pancreatic attacks?) seemed to have vanished. I reasoned that perhaps the medication had perpetuated the pain. Perhaps, in a perverse manner, my body had produced pain in order to get medicine. After all, I was addicted. Who knows to what ends an addicted body will go in order to get its "fix"? I proudly announced to one and all that I was physically cured of all my ills and would never again need to deal with the problem of pain.

I spoke far too soon, for out of nowhere, one blue-sky summer day, I was felled by the most agonizing, excruciating stomach pains. As bad as I had ever had. And as scary.

I didn't know what to do. I began to panic and the more I panicked the more my stomach hurt. Frantically, I telephoned Dr. Zuckerman. (I knew he would never offer me a tranquilizer or a painkiller. What I hoped he would offer me was help.)

"Take a Tylenol," he said, "and let me know how you feel tomorrow." I felt dejected. Tylenol, I knew, would have no effect. Far stronger medicines had failed. But I would try.

As the hours passed, the pain grew in intensity. By now I was sweating profusely, my hands were icy, and my abdomen was swollen.

I telephoned the doctor once more. "Take a hot bath, use a heating pad, take more Tylenol. And call me tomorrow."

I did all of those things. By 1:00 A.M., I was thrashing about in agony. My back felt as though it would break in two, and I couldn't touch my stomach, not even to put a sheet over me. I telephoned Alan. Would he come to be with me? He would.

And then I phoned Dr. Zuckerman again. "You'll just have to go to the emergency room." And he hung up.

I couldn't go to an emergency room—I couldn't walk. I telephoned the Smithers night nurse. I must go, she told me. Otherwise I might drink. But I couldn't go because I couldn't move.

I put the heating pad to my tender stomach, and turned it as high as it would go, while Alan solicitously brewed me tea. Miraculously, after an hour or so, I fell into a fitful sleep. The pain had diminished. I had slept. The heat had done it.

The next day I phoned the doctor. I begged him to try to find out what was wrong and then find something to do about it. Quickly!

We did tests. Pancreas normal. But the pain? I was given a stomach relaxer that contained no tranquilizer to take at the very first sign of pain.

"But," I said, "I can't be left helpless again. You'll have to give me something to have in the house." "I won't do that," the doctor told me. "You'll have to settle for Tylenol."

"Doctor Zuckerman," I insisted, "I just won't ever be left in that situation again. You're going to have to give me something for emergencies." And so, reluctantly, this antidrug doctor gave me a prescription for three codeine tablets.

About a month later, it happened again. I took my relaxant immediately. The pains did not subside. I took a bath. They didn't go away. I knew the codeine was there. I didn't take it. What I did do was use the heating pad that had helped before. And, thank God, I got relief! I never have used that codeine to this day, though it is still there, should pain ever be unsupportable. So far, it never has been. Perhaps I don't panic because I know the doctor won't make me take more pain than I can bear.

It has been more than a year since that last stomach attack. I haven't
et had a recurrence. I don't anticipate one.

During the first summer of my sobriety, I came face to face with fear.
My father was seriously ill. He would need a major operation, and it
ould be a dangerous one. Chances were high that he would not live.
At first I didn't believe it. It couldn't be true! Not my wonderful,
ealthy, and energetic father. Surely there was nothing he couldn't
andle.

But I was to fly home at once. The operation was scheduled to take
lace within two days.

After I had wrestled with the concern about my father's condition—
etting reassurance that his doctor was the very best possible doctor,
hat the hospital was the very best hospital, and that his chances, right
ow, were the very best the chances would ever be—then I began to
orry about myself. Suppose my father died? How could I stand it?
What would I do? What would I take?

Weeping, I phoned Alan's friend Jenny (who was, by now, my friend
oo) and asked, "What am I going to do?"

"Well," she replied calmly, "one thing is sure. You won't take a
drink or a pill."

"But what if my father dies?"

And then she said another thing I will never forget. She said, "Sup-
ose your father dies. What is the very worst thing that could happen
o you?" It was the same question again. Reality. What would it be
ike? And then she continued, "Would you cry? Would you scream?
You might throw up. You might faint. But after those things, what
would be the worst thing that could happen?" And I had to answer—
othing. And it was all very clear. Nothing at all bad was going to hap-
en to me if I grieved normally. Even if I grieved abnormally. I wouldn't
ie. I might be sick. But nothing, absolutely nothing, really bad would
appen to me.

Jenny explained that if a person's natural grief is sedated, the agony
s prolonged. And the ensuing depression will last far longer than natu-
al grief that is worked through immediately.

And, for the first time in my life, I got the very clear picture: I no
onger had to sedate myself *no matter what happened.*

It was odd. I never knew I had that option before. I had lost many
eople in my life—family, friends, my young love. And yet no one had

ever said before, "You don't have to take anything." Sedation is generally a matter of medical course whenever there is grief.

The fact is, we are taught, from infancy, that we shouldn't feel pain, sadness, or grief, and we are surrounded by pretty little capsules (and physicians who believe they should administer them) that will take all those unpleasant feelings away, giving us instant psychic comfort.

We are bombarded with media messages that "relief is just a swallow away" and a lifetime of happiness is ours, if we'll only take our medicine. The message has come through loud and clear to most of us. We not only don't have to feel bad, we *should not* feel bad. And those powerful feelings of pain, sorrow, grief—all of the uncomfortable human emotions—must be swept away like cobwebs in a not-so-clean room. But by so doing, we also sweep away half of our humanity. For really living life entails experiencing *all* human feelings, both painful and joyous, and the cutting out of the unpleasant ones leaves us only half alive.

There's another important thing to remember. When you sedate one emotion, you sedate them all, and if you mute the pain, you also dull the joy. And you end up with no valleys, perhaps, but with no peaks, either. Life on one changeless emotional pitch isn't much of a life, after all.

My father, thank goodness, got well. But I'm just as glad I had to work through my future handling of grief. Because now I know it won't be through artificial tranquility.

Perhaps Dr. LeClair Bissell said it best: "There is no human problem that requires a chemical solution. A problem, after all, is not an illness."

Throughout all those insomniac years, when I routinely swallowed Placidyl, night after night, I never had any chance of sleeping well. Not as long as I took the medication. Because sleeping pills actually destroy natural sleep.

At a recent medical seminar, Dr. Stanley Gitlow, a New York psychotherapist (and, incidentally, an expert in the field of alcoholism) talked about the sleep-destroying effects of sleeping pills.

What such pills do is induce sleep unnaturally, and, in the process, disrupt the natural sleep patterns. REM (Rapid Eye Movement) sleep and Stage IV (the deepest and most restful sleep of all) disappear almost completely when the patient is taking sleeping medication. It takes weeks, often months, after such medication is halted, before sleep gets back to normal.

Dr. Gitlow tells of his own hospitalization, when he was offered the customary hospital sleeping pill. Although he faced surgery the next day and was feeling jittery, Dr. Gitlow refused the medication, rationalizing "If I take that, I'll sleep now, but I'll pay, with interest, later." For he would have paid for every night's sedated sleep with several nights' disturbed sleep, and that one pill would wreck his natural sleep patterns for days. Dr. Gitlow felt it was a price he couldn't afford.

Dr. LeClair Bissell points out that, after a short time, sleeping medication no longer works at all. Then the patient is "left with no sleeping pill that works and no natural sleep patterns to rely on." In short, sleepless.

And yet, eight-and-one-half million Americans took prescription sleeping pills in 1977, and about a quarter of those people took the pills nightly for two months or longer.

The definitive recent report on the problems associated with sleeping medications appeared in April of 1979. An expert panel of the National Academy of Sciences pronounced sleeping pills to be not as safe as many physicians believe and, furthermore, generally ineffective when used nightly for "more than a few days."

As reported in the *New York Times,* the panel said that sleeping pills should be used "for only a few nights at a time and should be prescribed in limited numbers. It is difficult to justify much of current prescribing of sleeping medication," said the report, which was prepared at the request of President Carter and stemmed from his concern over suicides and accidental deaths involving such drugs.

Dalmane is the most widely prescribed sleeping pill in this country, accounting for over fifty-three percent of all prescriptions, but even the manufacturer of Dalmane, Hoffman-La Roche, Inc., could only claim that their product is "safe and effective" for "up to twenty-eight days." And they, too, pointed out that "insomnia is a transient condition."

Even if you split the difference between the panel's time limit of "a few days" and the manufacturer's estimate of twenty-eight days, you still only come up with approximately a two-week period of effectiveness for any sleeping medication. But for every two-week period of sleep through medication, you just may be destroying your own natural sleep for months.

Which is, of course, exactly what happened to me. Over the years, I'd gone from mild to strong to stronger to strongest sleeping medication. By the time of my hospitalization, I was able to sleep only by taking a dangerous dose of pills. I always awoke exhausted and I was half-conscious all day. I felt terrible all the time. On the other hand, all the experts tell me that feeling terrible was miraculous in my case. I should have been dead.

Many people do die when they're on sleeping pills, and it isn't always because they took dangerous doses, either. Mixing pills or mixing booze with pills is playing Russian roulette. One of the most famous instances —the death of columnist Dorothy Kilgallen—happened, I hear, on a couple of Valium and a few drinks. The son of actor Paul Newman died after mixing Valium with alcohol. In neither case was anything like a suicidal overdose of pills taken, but the amount of drug in the body, combined with even a small portion of alcohol, had the cumulative effect of depressing the nervous system to the point where respiration ceased. Death.

Let's forget about extremes, however, and consider the fact that you want to be able to sleep—soundly and well. For as long as you continue to take pills to help you sleep, you won't. They'll put you out for a while, but then you will have to take more. And more. What then?

I wish I could tell you that as soon as I got off sleeping pills I slept soundly, but you've seen that wasn't the case. On the other hand, during the twenty-eight days I spent at Smithers, I began to sleep through the night.

The very fact that I abused my body with sleeping medications for years is bad enough, but when you consider not only the duration of abuse but the *amount* of abuse, isn't it a real wonder that my normal sleep patterns returned in only twenty-eight days? The resilience of the human body is amazing, indeed. In the course of getting my sleep patterns in order, however, I learned some very basic and very important things.

For one thing, I learned never to go to bed unless I was truly tired. Many years ago, one of my aunts had a nervous problem and wasn't sleeping. Her doctor told her never to go to bed out of boredom. That admonition came back to me the other day. It is something to keep in mind. If you are bored, then go out for a walk (physical fatigue is a first step to sound sleep), read a book, work on a hobby or whatever. Don't go to bed because you don't know what else to do!

Don't take your problems to bed! We all have problems. Everybody. One day I said to a Smithers counselor, "Why must everything be so hard for me? Why can't I just have things go smoothly, the way they seem to for everybody else?" And she said, "Everybody has something going wrong, all the time."

In Smithers we learned a slogan: "Turn it over." To the AA

members, it means "put it in the hands of your Higher Power." To me, that is God. To some, it may be fate, chance, whatever. But it means, simply, leave your problems to your own "Higher Power," who can solve them with no help from you. I have learned that, at least while I am in bed, I must "turn over" my problems. Then I am freed to sleep peacefully until day, when I can tackle those problems and realistically try to solve them.

I learned a lot of very practical tricks about sleep during my recovery. For one thing, the old folk tale about hot milk as a soporific is true after all. Milk works. I found that out while I was in Smithers. Later, when the Arabs were tuning up again, I discovered that warm milk—while it tastes pretty awful—does the trick twice as well.

There is a legitimate reason for milk's reputation as a soporific. It contains tryptophan, an amino acid that helps to produce serotonin—a biochemical manufactured in the body and critically involved in sleep. I only throw this information in so that you will not believe that milk's value is merely psychological. It *will* help you sleep.

Tryptophan can be purchased in capsule form (sold in drug stores as L Tryptophan) but—and this may be *my* psychological hangup—it did positively nothing for me. And so I always opt for the original. Milk.

The other thing that helped me out in the Arab crisis was a good, *hot* bath. I don't care how trite it all sounds. A very hot bath is relaxing and the hot-bath/warm-milk combination is a tried-and-true and guaranteed-by-me one.

Obviously, this only applies if your body is clean of sleeping medications. Otherwise, allow yourself a minimum of a month of unmedicated (and possibly restless) nights before you can expect these guaranteed results.

Back in my sleeping-pill days, I believed I *had* to sleep. I was sure that I would die if I didn't sleep. When, in the hospital, I tossed and turned for nights on end, I was convinced that my own end was near. It was not. I heard, over and over *ad nauseam,* that "nobody ever died from lack of sleep." It was small comfort to me then. It made me want to scream. But it is, nonetheless, true. Because when the body gets tired enough, it sleeps, no matter where it is or what the circumstances are. What we all have to learn is the patience to wait for sleep to come.

By that I don't mean the patience to lie, sleeplessly, tossing and turning in bed. If you've drunk your milk and had your hot bath and "turned over" your days' problems and given it a chance and still can't sleep . . . well, then, get up! You probably don't need as much sleep as you suppose. Research shows that, each year, the adult population of this country sleeps less and less. The average sleep period, by now, appears to be somewhere between six and seven hours per night. And, while during the last thirty years, average sleep has decreased, the average life expectancy has increased. There is no evidence to link the two, but, obviously, we aren't dying from too little sleep.

Now, I simply don't count hours. If I wake up early, it's OK. I have found that there are hundreds of thousands of people in New York who are out, happily jogging, in the dawn hours.

In my drugged days, I would have taken a 200-milligram Placidyl and rolled over for one more hour's sedated (and therefore useless) sleep.

I watch other insomniacs with sympathy now. "Why is it," I asked Alan one day, "that whenever you sleep at my house, you *sleep?* Soundly, I might add." He thought a minute, and then he said, "Because I know I have no alternatives."

What he meant was that at my house he knew he didn't have the option of taking a drink or a sleeping pill (God knows, I don't have any of *those* things around), and so he went to sleep and that was that. Which again makes me believe that plenty of insomniacs simply work pretty hard at convincing themselves of their own insomnia. When faced with an unsympathetic companion and no way out via sleeping medication, they turn over and fall asleep.

Which brings me to another point. Worry about sleep is what makes people sleepless in the first place. I have heard a friend say (seriously, too), "I have to go home early so I can start getting to sleep." I cringe when I hear such a statement. To make sleep into a compulsive ritual can only make it more difficult. Nobody said you have to sleep and nobody said you have to get a certain amount of sleep per night. Do not make preparations for going to sleep. Stay awake until you are tired (*Not* until you are bored—until you are tired.) Do all your preparations for bed early, so that you won't have to rouse yourself to wash your face, for example.

Though it seems elementary, I feel I must mention something you may be overlooking. The question of stimulation. Do you drink coffee all day? Colas? Tea? Do you eat your dinner late at night? Do you get involved in arguments or other stimulating conversation just before bed time? Do you watch exciting TV fare on late-night programs? Do you decide to do household chores or write letters before you retire?

Then you're over-stimulating yourself, all right. The body, after all requires a little time to get quiet before it can drop off into peaceful, restful sleep.

All you have to do is remember—and follow—these basic, simple rules. I promise you your sleep problems will disappear like magic:

1. Never make elaborate plans for going to sleep. Just wait until you're too tired to stay awake any longer. Then, and only then, get into bed.

2. Do all of your ablutions—face cleaning, hair-setting, etc.—well ahead of bedtime. You don't want to wake yourself up, now do you?

3. Never, never nap during the day. You're going to absolutely destroy your chances of sleeping at night if you do. Make yourself stay awake, no matter how tired you feel (the more tired, the better) until the bedtime hour.

4. When you get into bed, leave your problems behind. If a problem must be solved, deal with it well before sleep time. Then forget about it.

5. If at first you don't sleep, then just lie there. Good, quiet rest is almost as beneficial as sleep. (Chances are you'll be asleep before you know it.)

6. If you do find yourself tossing and turning for more than a half hour, get out of bed and do something—read, watch television. If you don't sleep tonight, you'll surely sleep tomorrow night.

7. If you awaken early and you feel bright-eyed and wide awake, get out of bed! No law says you have to lie there until a later hour. Who knows what you may discover by dawn's early light.

The most important rule of all, of course, is never, *never* take sleeping medication. Not if you want to sleep.

49.

"Didn't you sue your doctor?" everybody asked. And they were aghast when I said I not only had no plans to sue him, I was still seeing him. "But he got you addicted!" they accused. "No," I pointed out, "I got me addicted." He prescribed the pills; I swallowed them. But both he and I believed we were doing the right—and furthermore, the neces-sary—thing.

A doctor-patient relationship is a delicate thing. My relationship with my own doctor is an exemplary thing, I am told. But here is how that sort of relationship worked toward addiction.

He has been my doctor for more than twenty years—ever since I was an eager youngster fresh from Alabama. He has cared for me in sickness and in health, as the saying goes, and there is very little that I would not do for my doctor. You cannot know someone for all those years, through all the vagaries of life, without developing real affection for him. The doctor for the patient. The patient for the doctor. You either learn to love each other or you give up and move on to someone else.

I love my doctor. I believe he feels the same way about me. He wants to see me healthy and well. I believe that he is the person who can keep me healthy and well.

Unfortunately, a caring relationship between patient and doctor is the very relationship most likely to set up an addiction involvement. This is how it goes:

I told my doctor I felt sick. And I was tired of feeling sick. He knew, by then, that I had no patience with feeling bad. Furthermore, I knew that he knew how to fix me up. Please, couldn't he do it now? I really didn't have time to waste abed.

Sure, he knew how. He was well-trained. He was well-informed. He was up on all the latest developments in the vast and complicated world of medicine. He knew all of my medical peculiarities, having watched them develop over the previous twenty years. In fact there was nothing about my body he didn't know, from my peculiar allergies to my sometimes reverse reactions to medications. He knew all the tests I'd been given for whatever reasons, what the results had been, and how the puzzle fit together. He would do what he could to get me fixed up in a flash.

What he could do, of course, was what he had been trained to do in medical school, what he had been trained to do in internship, what he had been trained to do in residency, what he had been trained to do in all his many years of practice, and what he was still learning to do with every new break-through in medicine. He would give me the newest, and possibly most effective, of the appropriate medications. And then we would see. I should be cured very, very soon.

I, meanwhile, was growing more and more impatient. Within a few days I was phoning him again. Nothing was happening. Why wasn't it working? Couldn't he do something to make my cure faster? After all, I was a busy woman, I really didn't have time to spend being sick.

And so my doctor decided to try something else. Something newer. Something stronger. Something that might get me cured in a flash.

And so it went. And both he and I found out, the hardest possible way, the results of the practice of the best possible medicine.

My doctor is an excellent doctor. His credentials, and his reputation, are both impeccable. He is a careful doctor. And he would never, never want to harm me. But, by his medicine, I almost died.

Some believe I should blame my doctor. But I can't. He was, he believed, saving my life. He was, *I* believed, saving my life. So where did we both go wrong?

In the early months of my recovery, I was afraid to return to my own doctor. For one thing, I dreaded the confrontation. Sooner or later, I would have to ask him just how it all happened—*his* side of the story—and, oddly enough, I was afraid he would be angry and think I blamed him. For the time being, it seemed easier to avoid the situation.

Besides, I knew that Dr. Zuckerman was "safe." He would never prescribe anything that might be harmful to an addict like me. Grant you, Smithers had sent my doctor all the forms. ("Do not give this patient any tranquilizers, painkillers or other addictive drugs. If you have any questions, call us.") I'd mailed them myself. But in spite of them, I didn't feel like dealing with a potentially unpleasant situation. So I avoided my doctor.

Then, as the months wore on, I found that it didn't seem right, seeing someone else. No matter how kind that someone else was, my doctor was *my* doctor. I was the family for which he was the family doctor. I missed him. I missed his reassuring manner. And I missed having someone who already knew all about *me*.

The next time I needed medical attention (it would be nice to say I *never* needed medical attention again, but that wasn't, of course, the case), it was for a peculiar swelling in my throat. Just under my chin. My doctor spotted it at once—swollen salivary glands. He told me that it could be treated with antibiotics but it would, eventually, disappear all by itself. I said I'd give it time. Both of us were treading foreign terrain. I had never turned down an instant cure; he had never advised against one. Then we talked a bit. There was even more to his side of the story: he mentioned the need of the doctor to help by "doing something." But there are other factors at work.

One of the enormous problems the medical profession has in dealing with alcoholism and other addictions is the problem of recognition. I feel—and I told my doctor so—that most doctors are far too naive in their perceptions of the addiction disease. Probably because too few really view it as a true "disease" and not just an unsavory condition that ought to be hidden from view.

Also, for the most part, the denial inherent in the disease is often a question of actual non-recognition. The patient truly does not know, and therefore cannot believe, that he has become addicted, whether to alcohol or to another sedative drug.

I had no idea that I was a drug addict, and therefore my own denial of the fact was essentially a problem of awareness.

For example, I never got the same prescriptions from more than one doctor. Both my doctor and my shrink knew what I was taking. Both arranged for refills. And I never lied to either about that.

The fact was, neither had time to notice that the refills came more frequently than was safe. And when my doctor began to be a little concerned, I always managed to reassure him.

But, of course, I never told him that I took phenobarbital to help me stay within my six-Valium limit, or that I took codeine *with* Percodan, when neither seemed to work well enough alone. I fudged a bit on that. Now I see why. The addicted body has to get its drugs and it knows that. Without them, it might die. The brain gets a message to get the drugs, by any means. I got the drugs by not telling my doctor the whole truth—just the part I wanted him to hear—and in my addicted mind, I wasn't lying at all. But then that is the bizarre business of denial, and denial is what stands squarely between the addict and help.

It is a responsibility of the doctor, and the family and friends, to break through denial and point out addiction where it is seen.

But suppose the doctor does not see it?

Most doctors are untrained in alcoholism and addiction. Medical schools generally include about four hours of training in alcoholism, none, that I know of, in pill addiction.

But there are seminars and awareness programs available to physicians who feel a need to acquaint themselves more with the addiction problem. It seems obvious that almost every single doctor needs to know more. I don't think my own doctor, capable as he is, truly knows about withdrawal. I don't think many doctors do, unless they work in a hospital where addiction and alcoholism are oft-treated diseases. If the doctor has ever seen a patient in the severe stages of withdrawal, he is certainly going to think twice about prescribing the drug that has caused such misery.

I asked my doctor how he could justify prescribing, for example, Dexedrine for a dieting patient, knowing what he ought to know about that drug's addictive possibilities. His reply was that perhaps it was an immoral judgment on his part, but he preferred to be the doctor doing the prescribing, in the case of a patient who insisted on such a drug. That way he felt that he could at least have some control over the situation. A blunt refusal of the drug might send the patient into the arms of a disreputable drug-dealing doctor.

There is a lot to what he said. It is true that it is far better to have a patient on a *controlled* amount of any drug. But it is essential to explain to any patient the possibilities for addiction inherent in that drug and the excruciating agonies of withdrawal, if addiction comes.

I get furious whenever someone remarks "Gee! These doctors rake in a fortune off all these drugs!" That's just plain ignorance speaking.

There are, of course, some disreputable doctors who actually sell prescriptions, but these men are criminals and are usually brought to justice. Occasionally, doctors pander to patients (often wealthy or celebrity clients), prescribing for them any and all drugs they want. One such case made headlines when Dr. George C. Nichopolous, who for many years was part of singer Elvis Presley's retinue, had his license suspended by the Tennessee Board of Medical Examiners for indiscriminately prescribing and dispensing controlled substances. Dr. Nichopolous admitted prescribing ten thousand pills for Presley in the ten months preceding the singer's death.

Doctors like these, however, are the exceptions. I have never heard of any reputable doctor basing his office-visit fee on the number of prescriptions he writes. No, it makes absolutely no difference to his pocketbook whether you get the prescription or not.

The only difference is in the amount of time he spends with the patient. As one doctor put it, "It's a question of spending thirty seconds writing a prescription or thirty minutes explaining to the patient why she shouldn't have it."

The fact is that doctors today are terribly overworked. Some of them rely, to a great extent, on the drug company "detail men" to keep them abreast of the newest and best in medications. But such detail men are, in fact, no more than drug salesmen, and it is to their distinct advantage to soft-pedal any possible ill effects their product might produce. They are there to hard-sell their particular drug and they sure as hell aren't going to accentuate the negative.

When the doctor isn't hearing the salesman's pitch he is being bombarded with outrageous advertisements in the medical journals telling him how to solve the anxiety of the lonely (or overworked or newly divorced or newly wed) housewife by prescribing for her just the right little pill. The pharmaceutical industry, sadly, believes that most female problems are just "nerves" and therefore can be cured with tranquilizers. Sadly, too, most doctors seem to agree.

Many otherwise capable doctors admit that their practice simply does not allow them to spend the time necessary to discuss a patient's deep-seated anxieties. The best most doctors can do is to prescribe some sort of tranquilizer for immediate relief of anxious feelings. And the trouble begins.

50.

My life is very different now. For one thing, I am happy. I'm enjoying life with an enthusiasm I have not known since childhood. It is fabulous.

I am healthy. And I feel well, all of the time. Not just "unsick" but totally and completely, physically, marvelous. It is a great thing to be able to say.

Friends tell me I look better than I have in ten years. And they always add, "You look so calm." I am amused when they ask, "Are you on tranquilizers?" Of course they wonder why I laugh.

I look back on the past few years with astonishment and wonder about how I ever got my life into such a mess. But then, of course, I know. I wasn't in charge of that life—my addiction was. While I sat back and avoided responsibilities the sedative way. I've taken back those responsibilities now.

And I have learned that life never gives us more than we can handle in a single day and I've realized that I can handle whatever comes. So far I have.

Many of the little things that used to loom as "problems" in my life are pluses now. My apartment, for instance, still has the normal New York drawbacks—kitchen too small, price too big—but the same apartment that used to seem cold and isolated is now sunny, warm, lovable, and infinitely livable. I get a kick out of snuggling up to the big expanse of glass on the thirty-sixth floor, and the view is just fine.

My career is back on track and I am doing, I believe, the best work of my life. I no longer miss the old crowd down at the newspaper. Why should I? My friends have left for greener pastures. We have lunch often and they tell me how they envy my self-employed life. I don't blame them.

Every day, with very few exceptions allowed, I speak with other, recovered, addicts. My friends are my life-support system. Without them I would never be so well; we all survive by helping one another. It is what makes us feel that we are, indeed, the lucky ones. It is what makes us "grateful recovering addicts."

Which brings me to psychiatry. I have never gone back to my shrink. Not because I don't consider him a competent therapist—I do—but because I don't feel that psychiatry has the answers when it comes to dealing with addiction.

As Dr. LeClair Bissell so beautifully put it, "If the house is on fire, you don't look for the arsonist. You put out the fire first." So it is with addiction. Twenty years spent in therapy searching for the reason you have an addictive personality won't cure you. First you must arrest the addiction. Later on, when you're recovered, you will have plenty of time to ponder the causes of it all. But arresting the addiction requires the expertise of those schooled in treating that disease—the addiction specialists. I would never trust my own life to anyone less qualified.

In my weekly therapy group, we are all addicts together. Whatever other problems we deal with, we never forget that addiction is our real problem. Deal with the addiction, and every other problem can be solved.

It may sound like oversimplification. It isn't.

I have kept in touch with some of my Smithers classmates. The news has not always been cheerful.

Gus has been in three rehabilitation centers in the past year. He is, for the moment, sober.

Gloria left Smithers and went into outpatient therapy. She lasted only six weeks and is taking her amphetamines again. I don't talk to her now.

The loud-mouthed salesman is back in a rehabilitation center, where he is to remain for six months.

The surgeon lost his license for falsifying prescriptions.

Sigrid divorced her husband and landed a job on a fashion magazine. She is soon to marry a bright, politically ambitious lawyer. She has been sober ever since Smithers.

The prissy schoolteacher was hospitalized eight times after her release from Smithers. Then she plunged from a twelfth-floor window to her death.

The oil executive has become senior vice-president of his company. He attends group therapy twice a week.

The ex-prizefighter is drinking and living in a doorway on the Bowery.

Ruby Begonia had her crippled arm and leg surgically corrected. She is sober and working again.

Nobody has heard a word from Becky.

Happily, nobody has heard a word about Maxine.

As for my own life, well, I wish I could tell you it has been a bed of roses. It hasn't. For example, Alan and I didn't walk into the sunset together. Alan drank. I didn't. And although we tried to adjust to each other's lives, the relationship grew more strained with time. "It has to be over," I cried to my group. "Yes, it does," they agreed. "It will never work. Alan has a drinking problem." But I didn't really want to believe that.

Then one day, Alan's friends told me he was in love with someone else. I thought the best thing to do was ask Alan. With trembling hands, I dialed his number.

"Are you in love with someone?"

"Yes."

"Is it serious?"

"Yes. But I still love you, too. You can love two people, you know. It's a different kind of love, but . . ."

I put the receiver down. From somewhere deep there came a cry. It grew until it filled the room. It was my own voice. And I knew I had heard that voice before, ten long years ago.

But this time, things were different. This time I didn't take a drink and I didn't take a pill. This time I cried for a very long time and it was over. The long, unhappy relationship between Alan and myself. I haven't seen him since.

There is, however, another man in my life. He doesn't look mean and evil; he looks kind and gentle and humorous and intelligent. I don't know where this relationship will lead me, but I'm living it and loving it as it happens, exactly one day at a time.

I am, of course, still an addict fighting her addiction and I have to be constantly on my guard. My disease hasn't been cured; it's only in remission, and every day, in hundreds of silly ways, it reminds me of its power. Sometimes I find myself popping a Tylenol into my mouth when I don't really need it. Or dashing out to buy more milk, when there's a full quart in my refrigerator. Acting every bit the addict all the time.

But now I have all the help I need. I have my wonderful, supportive friends, who share their lives, hopes, troubles, and dreams with me and who listen, in turn, to mine.

I have my beautiful family, and we've never been closer than now.

I have my Smithers therapists, who twice a week, take me by the hand and lead me down the rocky road to my new and hopeful life. It's never easy. But then nothing worth having is.

I can see the changes in myself. My friends can, too, and when they say to me, "You're so different, Mary Ann," I get a thrill I never got from any chemical.

I know that nothing is as important to me as my sobriety and I must allow no one, no thing, to interfere with the sobriety I almost gave my life to find.

I also know that for what I do with this brand-new life, I alone am responsible. That is a very nice feeling.